D1239420

Concepts of Engineering
System Design

Concepts of Engineering System Design

WARREN E. WILSON
Chairman of Engineering
Harvey Mudd College
Claremont, California

McGraw-Hill Book Company

new york   st. louis   san francisco   toronto   london   sydney

Concepts of Engineering System Design

Preface

During the last several years many engineering educators, including particularly the author of this text, have become increasingly dissatisfied with the frequent failure of lower division courses to orient the student to the engineering profession of today. It is customary to expose this student to courses in science and mathematics, with a very minimum of engineering for at least one of the two years. Realization that it might be desirable to bring to the student earlier an appreciation and understanding of engineering resulted in the establishment of courses directed toward his orientation in this field. This text has been developed through use in such a course.

Historically, the approach in the lower division in an engineering college has been to introduce the engineering student to the profession through a course in graphics. This was not often a successful approach. The student obtained an erroneous view of the work of the engineer and the significance of the profession. He was introduced to his lifetime career through the work of the technician, and his reaction was frequently and understandably negative.

In order to avoid the difficulties inherent in such an approach, the present text assumes that the engineering design of a system is of major interest to a student who is seriously considering a career in this field. It introduces him to the concept of the profession and the functions inherent in the design of a system.

Early in the text the student is introduced to the tools available to the engineer. Powerful mathematical methods are described, and their use in rather elementary problems is illustrated. No effort is made to develop with great rigor this mathematical background; instead, the student is led to familiarity with the mathematics through relatively simple applications. No concern about the adequacy of the student's mathematical background is necessary in either the freshman or sophomore year, since the development of the subject is at a very elementary level.

Emphasis is placed on the fact that many problems with which the engineer is confronted are open-ended and have no single correct solution; rather, they have many solutions, and it is the task of the engineer to select the solution or solutions that are optimum with respect to the criteria established for the evaluation of the solutions. Most of the problems in the text are of this type. They have no single correct answer. Indeed, there may not be an acceptable answer. In this case, restating the problem may be a very useful exercise for the student.

It is suggested that this text be used in an introductory course, the primary objective of which is orientation in the freshman year. On the other hand, it can be used in the sophomore year as a first course in system engineering; it may also have some value for the engineer who wishes to keep in touch with engineering developments but does not have a very strong background in mathematics. He can follow the presentation of this text and understand the significance of system design as it is approached today. The objective, insofar as the student's education is concerned, is rather more weighted toward motivation, the exciting of curiosity, and an appreciation of the difference between the problems in mathematics and science which have straightforward solutions and the engineering problem which may have no solution or many solutions, as the case may be. A special effort is made to show that the engineer frequently does not have available all the information and data that would be desirable to obtain a suitable solution to his system design problem; that he must make decisions on the basis of minimal information and with no certainty that a best solution has been obtained.

In the development of this text, the author is deeply indebted to the staff and faculty of the department of engineering at Harvey Mudd College. Those who participated in the freshman system engineering course have rendered invaluable service in completing the manuscript. Particular thanks are due to two members of the department who wrote portions of the text. Professor James Monson prepared most of the material on the analog computer. Credit for the method of presentation must go to him, but any errors are the responsibility of the author. Professor Sedat Serdengecti devised the method of presenting the material on sensitivity of a feedback system, and credit for an elementary method which at the same time has rigor is certainly due him. If there are errors of detail, the author assumes responsibility for them. Professor Serdengecti also rendered valuable assistance in the preparation of the material on information processing. To Mrs. Norma Kruger goes deepest appreciation for her skill and patience in typing the manuscript many times to bring it to its final form.

Warren E. Wilson

Contents

CHAPTER 5   Mathematical Models and Methods

CHAPTER 6   Tools of Optimization

CHAPTER 7   Feedback Control

Evolution of the Profession of Engineering

1.1. Definitions   Twentieth-century Western civilization is technologically based. It contrasts with the agrarian civilizations of the past and with the contemporary Eastern civilizations that have not developed a comparable technology. Technology has been defined as the systematic knowledge of the industrial arts; it has also been said to include both man-made physical objects and the techniques associated with them. Technology involves, therefore, the materials of which an object is made and the tools, machines, skills, and procedures used to make it.

Among the members of a highly developed technological society are those who are skilled in the various professions and trades that contribute to the technology. We shall devote our attention primarily to one of these groups, namely, the professional engineers. The engineer is a practitioner of the art of engineering and is closely associated in his work with both the scientist and the technician.

The words engineering, engineer, science, scientist, and technician are all in common use but, unfortunately, they are widely misunderstood.

Science includes the search for facts about our physical world and the formulation of hypotheses that make possible the prediction of physical events under prescribed conditions. The scientist devotes himself professionally to research, the discovery of new facts about the physical nature of the universe, and to the synthesis of hypotheses to predict physical phenomena.

Engineering is the professional activity that employs the materials and forces of nature to devise the best and most efficient machines and systems for the use of mankind. The engineer devotes his efforts to such useful items with due regard for the economics of their production and their impact on the civilization in which he lives.

The technician assists the engineer in his work and is thoroughly familiar with the technology with which he is associated. Generally speaking, his work is similar to that of the engineer but at a very different level. The relationship of the nurse to the physician in the field of medicine is analogous to that of technician to engineer. He is an arranger rather than a composer, to use an analogy with music.

1.2. The Evolving Roles of Engineering and Science in Technology

At the beginning of the twentieth century, there was a time lag of 25 to 50 years between the discovery of a new scientific fact and its practical application. This time lag has been reduced steadily and at mid-century was about 5 years.

During the nineteenth century, it took nearly 25 years for the known physical facts of electricity and mechanics to result in practical items of use to man. However, the facts that established the possibility of a nuclear explosion were discovered in 1939, and in 1945 the first nuclear explosion took place. This was a total of 6 years from basic discovery to practical application. There was an even shorter interval between the basic discoveries necessary for the synthesis of a transistor and its commercial production. Although it is impossible to reduce the time lag to zero, it has been shortened to less than 5 years, particularly in the case of the tunnel or Esaki diode. The concept of this device was first reported by Esaki in January, 1958.[1] Within 2 years the diode was available commercially in pilot-line quantities.[2]

[1] Leo Esaki, *Phys. Rev.,* vol. 109, pp. 603–604, Jan. 15, 1958.
[2] R. N. Hall, Tunnel Diodes, *IRE Trans. Electron Devices,* vol. ED-7, pp. 1–9, January, 1960.

One might note at this point that, while a zero or negative time lag is impossible, by definition, nevertheless there have been, and will continue to be, examples of engineering applications in which certain features of our technology anticipate scientific discovery—an apparent negative time lag.   In the earlier years of industrial development in the West, technological application consistently preceded scientific discovery in a peculiar sense.   For example, there was a steam engine before the laws of thermodynamics and heat transfer were thoroughly understood.   The concept of a force exerted by an expanding gas was sufficient to make the steam engine possible.   Optimizing its performance awaited elaboration of the laws of thermodynamics and heat transfer, and optimization of performance is the essence of engineering application.

To summarize, technological application of known facts can take place before all the details that will permit optimization of design are thoroughly understood.   As the sophistication of the application increases, more scientific facts must be available before optimization is possible.   Furthermore, optimization of design is the distinguishing feature of the professional-engineering approach to the problems of satisfying man's needs.   A popularized version of this concept is that "An engineer can do for one dollar what anyone can do for two."

The reduction of the time lag has resulted in new relationships in research and application.   Basic-research workers frequently continue on a specific project, applying the results of their studies in a practical way.   The urgency of many developments has precipitated this situation.   This is particularly true in the military area where it is necessary to have available during the development stages people who are thoroughly familiar with the scientific basis of the technique.

Creative engineering effort directed toward the development of new and better devices for the use of man now calls for greater research effort than was needed a century ago. From approximately 1850 to 1930, an engineer could create most of the needed devices and systems, using nothing much more sophisticated than a handbook of engineering or, at most, a textbook in mechanics or electrical theory. He had on hand a stock of knowledge and tools to be applied to the design of the most complex component or system that might be required.   The application of new scientific data to more complex systems creates the need for more exact knowledge and frequently for knowledge not currently available. The only practical way in which this need can be satisfied is by means of a research investigation.

The scientist pursues basic research to acquire knowledge for its own sake, whereas the engineer initiates research to produce currently needed information. Economic considerations usually preclude engineering research if no need exists. However, industry justifies research that may yield useful results in future applications and, indeed, carries on large programs of this kind. Thus we distinguish between basic research and applied research. The research is not different in itself, nor are the methods of prosecuting it different; rather, the motivation for it is different. The scientist, whether a basic scientist or an applied scientist, provides information that the engineer must have when creating new devices and systems.

The engineer requires the services of technicians who are thoroughly familiar with the technology of rather narrowly specialized areas. They are educated to the general level of the engineer in the early twentieth century, when specialization was the order of the day, and can do routine testing and design in their special fields. Today the professional engineer requires a broader and deeper scientific background and knowledge of the current technology.

At mid twentieth century, the objectives of American industry and military technology have caused changes in emphasis on research and development. Civilian industry has, in general, concentrated on reducing the costs of production and on the gradual evolution of product design. A modest research effort has been made to provide necessary information, but industry's development overall has called for a relatively small research effort in contrast with the very large and costly one associated with the military and aerospace industries.

The latter's emphasis on research follows naturally from the lack of knowledge characteristic of an industry operating at a frontier. Certainly no handbooks are available. Demands for reliability are very high in both the military and aerospace, and there is less concern with economics. In general, although there are exceptions, the two aspects of American industry, the military-aerospace and the strictly civilian, are quite different in their engineering emphasis. A major portion of engineering effort in aerospace and military is devoted to research, whereas the civilian branch of industry concentrates more on design and production at the lowest possible cost.

The reduction in time lag and the emphasis on research are two important features of the development of engineering, but there is a third, most significant contribution of the engineering profession of recent years. This is the concept of system engineering. A wholly satisfactory definition of system engineering does not seem to exist at this time. However, the concept is reasonably well stated by the following: "The performance of a physical system depends upon that of all its components, but transcends that of any one portion."[1] The essence of this concept is that system performance cannot be determined from the performance of its individual components alone. A system's characteristics are more than the sum of the characteristics of its components and are derived from the nature of the interconnection of the individual elements.

The role of the engineer in system engineering is creative design in the broadest sense, involving responsibility for the ultimate functioning of the system. System engineering differs specifically from older concepts of engineering in the formality, breadth, and completeness of the consideration given to design. Systems differ in being larger, more complex, and in many cases automatic. Among the most important features of the design procedure are the formulation of a mathematical model, the analysis of the sensitivity of the system with respect to its elements, the analysis of the compatibility of the various components and subsystems, the determination of the stability of the system when subjected to various inputs, optimization of the design with respect to some preselected criterion, prediction of the performance of the system, and the evaluation and testing of the system by means of a mathematical model or prototype.

The rapid development of electronic and electrical systems, together with powerful analytical tools for the study of stability and prediction of performance, has produced a great body of data and techniques applicable to systems in general. The realization that systems have many characteristics in common, regardless of the nature of their components and functions, has led to very powerful general methods of attack on problems of system design.

Some of the most important and rapid advances occurred in the analysis and design of feedback control systems that are basically electrical and electronic. It was very soon realized that these methods could be applied to mechanical, pneumatic, and hydraulic sys-

[1] Richard W. Jones, System Theory and Physiological Processes, *Science,* vol. 140, no. 3566, pp. 461–464, May 3, 1963.

tems, and later they were applied to systems of totally different nature. Application to physiological systems is one of the most recent new developments.

1.3.   Systems and Their Characteristics

In the broadest sense, system engineering is concerned with the synthesis and analysis of the performance of physical systems, with or without automatic feedback control, which are optimized with respect to accepted criteria.

The concept that the performance of a system transcends the performance of its components is illustrated by Figs. 1.1 and 1.2. Figure 1.1 shows a system for loading a container to a predetermined total weight of liquid, with provision for automatic shutoff when the proper amount of liquid has accumulated. It is apparent that, as the liquid flows into the container at the rate Q units of volume per unit time, the downward force exerted on the spring increases, and consequently the arm OA moves downward. This, in turn, actuates the valve and tends to close it as the point A moves downward. If the spring has been properly selected and if the valve, arm, and spring are properly oriented, the valve shuts off when the specified weight of liquid has flowed into the container.

We consider, now, the components of this system. There is a pipe, a valve, the arm OA, the spring, and the container with its supporting cables. It is apparent that the valve alone cannot perform

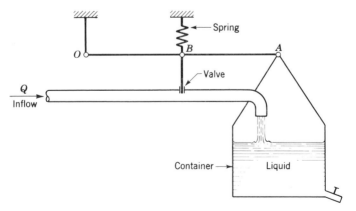

Fig. 1.1   Liquid loading system.

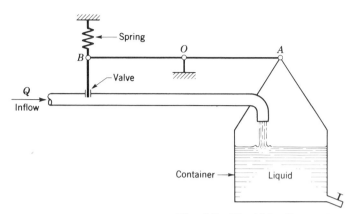

Fig. 1.2 Liquid loading system.

the desired function; it must be actuated by some outside agency. It is also clear that the arm *OA* by itself can perform no function that would result in measuring a given quantity of liquid. The spring is capable simply of exerting a force in proportion to its extension. The container, quite obviously, is incapable of performing any of the necessary functions other than that of containing the liquid. However, when these various components are connected as shown in Fig. 1.1, they produce the desired result.

To illustrate that the method of connecting the components is of prime importance, let us consider Fig. 1.2, where only one change has been made. The spring, valve, and bar *OA* have been reoriented. The fulcrum *O* is now at the middle of the bar, and as the weight of the liquid increases, the point *A* moves downward and the point *B* moves upward. The spring restrains the motion of the point *B*. As more liquid flows into the container, the valve no longer closes; rather, it actually opens. As the weight of liquid continues to increase, the valve opens further. If this system were placed in operation, it would fail completely to attain the desired objectives; in fact, it would not even start to operate if the valve were closed when there was no liquid in the container. There would be nothing to open the valve, whereas, in the case of Fig. 1.1, the valve is open if there is no weight or at least not sufficient weight in the container to close it. The latter system does not provide for continuous operation in filling and emptying the container, but it illustrates the elements of a very simple, partially automatic system which, when properly connected, performs the desired function. When improperly connected, it does not do so.

Large, complex, and automatic systems must be distinguished carefully from older systems that were well engineered but lacked characteristics inherent in modern automatic systems. For example, a city sewage-disposal system or a water-supply system may be complex but it need not be fully automatic.

Inherent in the operation of an automatic system is the feedback control. Not only does the system function automatically but, in addition, it is controlled by feedback of information to assure that the output is the desired one. The best single example of a modern, complex, automatic system is the telephone system of the United States. This system is, without question, large and complex, and it is approaching completely automatic operation. That such a system has these features and, in addition, has performance characteristics not evident from its single components is easily illustrated by contrasting the original telephone, in use 50 years or more ago, with the present-day system. The old telephone operated in a very simple manner. The user raised the receiver, and eventually a response came from the operator inquiring "Number, please." The caller gave the number to the operator, and she, by very simple mechanical manipulations, connected the line of the caller to the line of the person called. The bell on the called person's telephone rang, and eventually there might be a response.

Today, where automatic dialing is available, the caller raises the receiver and, if he operates the device properly, waits for a particular sound, the "dial tone," before he begins dialing. He then dials the number, and the system begins an automatic process of great complexity. This complexity stems not from the difficulty of connecting the two lines but, rather, from the necessity for meeting various eventualities that may arise during the calling of a number.

With a human operator, the caller simply waited to hear the operator's voice before he gave his number. If the operator were very busy, the waiting time would be long. With automatic dialing it is necessary either to provide such a large number of devices that there will be no waiting at all times or to restrain the caller, as is now done, and somehow to optimize the situation. It is practically impossible to provide an essentially infinite number of means to respond to the caller; hence some kind of signal must inform the caller when the system is ready to take his call. This, in itself, is not a simple procedure. After the number has been dialed, the system must determine if there is a line available to call the desired number and, after the number has been called, note if that line is free or is already busy. If it is busy, the caller must be informed of this automatically.

While the operation of the automatic dial system is so familiar that we seldom think of its inherent complexity, we occasionally learn of some of the problems. At holiday times the loads on the long-distance lines are very heavy. A caller may get a rapid connection with the local portion of the telephone system. However, as the system hunts for a long-distance trunk line, it finds that they are all busy, and the caller is so informed.

If a very large number of people in any one community should decide to use their phones at one time, the present installation could not accommodate them all. This situation could arise in case of emergency. It is therefore necessary to design into the system some means of selection. Under normal operation, this is done at random. There is no assurance that calls will be made in the order of their initiation. In case of emergency, the telephone company has a different procedure that will give priority to certain previously designated callers.

The fact that users may not perform in the proper manner creates additional problems in a system as complex as the telephone system. Users are admonished to wait for the dial tone. If one does not do so, there must be a response that will prevent chaos in the system. Perfect performance by all callers cannot be expected; hence the system must be designed to handle unusual situations. One may, for example, decide to make a telephone call, raise the receiver, listen for the dial tone and begin to dial a number, and then, in the midst of the dialing operation, decide not to complete the call and hang up. If this had not been anticipated in the design, one line would be out of operation for an unreasonable period of time. On the other hand, if the system is designed to make a suitable response, the line is disconnected when the dialing ceases and does not resume after a prescribed period of time.

Traffic-control systems of large cities are familiar features of Western civilization. In most cases, such systems grew from individual signal lights at intersections to systems integrated into a single unit, as that of Denver, Colorado.   Probably none was designed as a system from the start.

The most difficult aspect of traffic-control system design is to define the best system for a particular situation.   This is no simple matter.   Some criterion must be selected for measuring the quality of the traffic control.   High speed for each individual car going through the city might be selected as the criterion of optimum operation.   However, under many circumstances, high speed of individual cars does not necessarily result in the largest total load through the system, as spacing increases with speed but not linearly.   To control traffic at a street intersection, one might arbitrarily decide that the traffic in one direction should be allowed to flow for a period of time equal to twice that of flow in the other direction.   Then very good flow would be likely on the street with the longer time, but very undesirable traffic jams in the other direction might be possible.   A more promising solution would be to optimize by minimizing the sum of the waiting times in the two directions.

The traffic-control system of an entire city presents many much more complex problems to be solved.   The changes in traffic density throughout the day, and from day to day, require that the system be adaptable.   In the most sophisticated systems the intervals of time between changes in traffic flow are automatically controlled in response to sensing devices that measure the flow of traffic throughout the city and are programmed to optimize the flow in some respect.   The facts that the space between vehicles increases as speed increases and that human reaction time is not zero lead to optimum speeds to carry maximum traffic loads.   The spacing-speed relationship and reaction time to commands for stopping and starting of traffic flow result in complex relationships that require very careful study in order to attain the optimum.

Many of the most complex, and from a technical standpoint the most interesting, systems are military in nature.   These are sometimes called conflictive systems.   An offensive system ultimately comes in contact with a defensive system if military action takes place.   Systems are therefore designed to annihilate each other.   This characteristic, in addition to all those inherent in a nonmilitary system, complicates the design.   Optimization of the performance of a military system depends, as does optimization in a civilian system, upon the objective of the system.

The function of a part of a military system might be to detect the approach of enemy aircraft or missiles and give suitable warning. This requires an extensive communication system and each element must be designed so that it will resist enemy attempts to jam or destroy it.   It is highly desirable that such systems be so designed that, as conditions change, they can adapt to the new environment.   A complete military system might consist of a means for detecting the approach of enemy attack, notification of suitable authorities of this attack, and reception of commands from these authorities to launch an attack against the enemy.   This system would have characteristics representing a great deal more than the simple sum of the various components that form the system, and evaluation of its performance would be critical.

In each case, establishment of a criterion for judging the quality of performance and for optimization is imperative but difficult.   In the first case, sensitivity to the approach of any object is desirable, but discrimination in selecting among these objects to decide which are dangerous and which are harmless is equally important.   In the second case, the criteria for judging performance must include proper determination of both the danger of not anticipating an attack and the danger of precipitating defensive action when none is called for.

1.4.   Significance of System Engineering

The concept of system engineering is new and is the most important recent achievement of engineering, not only as a technique of engineering design and creative professional effort in our technology but also as a discipline with the potential of many applications in other fields.   This point is well illustrated by the following quotation: "The physiologist is not apt to become an engineer, for, as the saying goes, you cannot make a silk purse out of a sow's ear; but the physiologist can learn from engineering an enormous amount of pure physiology that he cannot learn from any other source."[1]   Gray goes on to discuss the roles of physics and chemistry in the development of the concepts of physiology, and then notes:

> For centuries, it has been the avowed goal of physiology to understand how the living organism works or functions.   It is

[1] John S. Gray, A Physiologist Looks at Engineering, *Science,* vol. 140, no. 3566, pp. 464–466, May 3, 1963.

still the goal today when the engineer's instruments, techniques, and concepts are brought to bear on the age-old problem. There is one difference, however. This latest addition to the armamentarium promises to be more effective than its predecessors in helping physiology attain one of its goals.

He then illustrates the usefulness of certain engineering techniques in understanding the physiological system as follows:

The discovery that the principles of control systems so beautifully worked out by engineers can be fairly directly translated into fundamental principles of physiology was an exciting one. Knowledge of the principles of control systems sheds a penetrating light on the behavior of physiological systems, results in a more powerful approach, and reorients one's outlook to such a degree that all one's thoughts, experiments, and teachings in physiology are affected.

The potential for the application of system engineering is essentially limitless, for example, the design of a transportation system for an entire nation or continent. However, it must be recognized at the outset of such an undertaking that the choice of criteria must be the concern of the citizenry and the optimization of performance is the province of the engineer. The establishment of civic goals, standards of quality and beauty, and other aesthetic or moral considerations must precede the engineering design. Within constraints so imposed and with established criteria, a design of quality can be produced.

1.5. Engineering Function and Methods

In order that technology progress, civilian goods must be produced in sufficient quantity to satisfy the needs, and the products must be of such quality and design that the customer will buy them with satisfaction. If the standard of living is to be raised, the real cost of the product to the consumer must decrease. To attain higher quality and reduced cost of consumer products, the means of production must be continually improved. Machinery must be ever more productive and provide goods at lower cost. The development of automatic machines and systems, commonly called automation, has been a consequence of this process.

The role of the engineer in a developing technology is that of the creator of new and better products, tools, and machines. In civilian industry he is concerned with production at low cost. In the aerospace and military industries there is less emphasis on the economics and more emphasis on the novelty and reliability of the new system or component.

The necessity for emphasis on low cost, better quality, and high rates of production of consumer goods is obvious. In aerospace activity, new instruments and machines are necessary since only a meager technology exists in this area. The challenge, therefore, is largely in creating new devices—not necessarily optimum ones, in any sense, with respect to either economics or performance. In the case of the military, optimization of defensive or offensive ability is desired. Once again cost is not the primary consideration.

The engineer must assume responsibility for the production of either a system, a device, or a tool. A project leading to this goal proceeds much in the following manner: First, the problem is stated as a requirement to design a system or device. The feasibility of accomplishing the objective is evaluated in what is called a feasibility study. If the result of the study is unfavorable, the project is scrapped, or the problem is restated. If the study indicates a possibility of attaining the objectives, then one of several things may happen. If the feasibility is low, there may be need for a great deal of research or for redefining the objectives. If the feasibility is high, the project can continue directly. In any case, once feasibility has been established, a preliminary design is undertaken. A broad outline for the prosecution of the project is made. Orders of magnitude are established, areas of uncertainty are mapped out, rough cost estimates are obtained, and a crude time schedule is set up. At this point, the need for information is stated and areas of research are suggested.

If the preliminary design indicates that the project should continue, action is taken in several areas. Research is carried out to secure information in those fields where it is lacking. Parts of the project may be designed in detail even though others must await new data to be obtained through research. The stage between preliminary design and final design is called development. It is a combination of research effort, preliminary design, and such final design as is possible.

When a design has reached the point where it seems feasible to undertake construction of a prototype, or at least portions or components of the prototype, this is done. Upon completion of a prototype, with or without complete data, as the case may be, test and evaluation of the model are made. If, at this stage, one is concerned primarily with a number of components, these can be tested in an orderly fashion. Following this, a combination of the components of the system in the form of a prototype must be evaluated. This presents much greater problems than the simple test of the component parts, because of difficulty in establishing criteria and in carrying out large-scale tests. After test and evaluation, it is almost inevitable that some redesign will be necessary to correct faults found during the development. In fact, the sequence of test, evaluation, and redesign may continue through several cycles until the form of the prototype is satisfactory. Then final design is begun, incorporating all the refinements indicated by the prototype construction, test, and evaluation. The final design is then passed on to production or construction, as the case may be—construction if there is to be a single product and production if it is to be mass-produced. After construction is complete or production has continued for some time, operation and maintenance begin.

Throughout the life of the project, the engineer is responsible for its overall success. The engineer in charge will have on his staff engineers who are specialists in certain areas, technicians who are masters of certain phases of the technology, and applied scientists expert in research. The project engineer's responsibility is to see that the project is successfully coordinated and executed throughout. Every member of the team must be aware of the significance of the device or system to be produced. It is not enough that each be a narrow specialist in a feature of the design; rather, he must know the function of the product, its effect on the environment, and the effect of the environment on it. He must be continually conscious of cost. The project engineer must guide the design with optimization in mind, producing the best possible design in terms of the stated objectives. His responsibility calls for a high level of ability in decision making, a responsibility that he cannot shirk.

1.6. Engineering Problems in Today's Technology

The engineer in the late twentieth century must seek solutions of problems in the civilian area and in the aerospace and the military sectors. The problems of the latter two are reasonably well known and are the subject of headlines of the daily press. Less well known, but equally pressing for mankind, are problems of the civilian economy. These problems will engage the highest talents of the engineer during the next century. In order to attack them successfully, the engineer must be fully familiar with the scientific background of the day, be cognizant of the mathematical tools available, be aware of the sociological and economic problems involved, and, above all, have a sincere appreciation of the impact of technology on human civilization and culture.

As observed by Dean J. Douglas Brown of Princeton University:[1]

> The central attribute of a learned profession is thus responsibility, not for a segmented detail of a total problem, but for an effective solution of the total problem. This means for the profession of engineering that the days are past when each specialist can withdraw into his specialty and become a servant of someone else's grand design.
>
> The time has come for engineering statesmanship on a far broader scale than ever before. Past examples of such statesmanship, such as TVA, the Golden Gate Bridge, the Panama Canal, great dams, and industrial complexes are many and justify a high sense of accomplishment. The problems which engineers must help solve in the future are in part those which engineers helped to create—the congestion of our cities, the dangerous crowding of our highways and airways, the fouling of our atmosphere, gross fads in building design, and the disruptions of sudden technological change. For example, I would claim that the present condition of Los Angeles, New York, and Altoona, Pa., is the result in large part of inadequate engineering statesmanship. I will throw in the Newark meadows and a few thousand acres of slums. If engineers can design space ships to go to the moon, why can't they design a safer automobile? Who is to be the bridge between science and human fulfillment—the professional engineer or the Madison Avenue pollster?

[1] J. Douglas Brown, Your Learned Profession, *Mech. Eng.,* vol. 85, no. 4, p. 43, April, 1963.

Among the problem areas of major concern, requiring the highest order of engineering talent, are the following:

1. Water supply
2. Air pollution
3. Communication
4. Transportation
5. Food supply
6. Exhaustion of natural resources

We shall consider each of these in some detail, delineating the background of the problem, possible solutions, and the relation of these problems to modern civilization.

Water supply is inadequate, except in very rare instances, in locations supporting a highly developed technological civilization. The demands for industrial and individual use are growing so rapidly that they are outstripping the supply to be derived from the usual sources. It has been traditional to use lakes or rivers as water supplies. More recently, attempts have been made to render sea water fit for human use. Serious proposals are being made for purification of water that has been used once and passed through a sewage-treatment system. The cost of processing sea water is high and will probably remain so for many years, although undoubtedly increased demand and reduction in cost will make feasible the use of processed sea water in the foreseeable future. In fact, except for reprocessed sewage, there is really no other source with sufficient potential to satisfy the expected demand if population continues to increase as it is at mid-century.

The pollution of air by man-made devices has caused serious problems in many cities. Los Angeles, notably, has a smog problem that will press for solution within a decade or two. Since this pollution comes from industrial processes and automobiles, the solution must be found either by removing the source of pollution or by treating the air or the effluent from industrial plants and automobiles. This is a problem involving economics and human relations to a degree that is taxing the engineer's ingenuity. It is difficult to convince the automobile owner that he should assume the responsibility for pollution of the air and incur the costs necessary for its elimination. Possible solutions lie in treatment of the exhaust, treatment of the fuel itself, change to a different fuel, or perhaps abandonment of the automobile as a means of commuter transportation. Any one of these possibilities poses, for the engineer, problems that are not easy of solution.

Problems of communication arise in the telephone system, in the storage and retrieval of information, and in radio and television. The telephone system is the largest and most complex of our modern systems. The major problems in communication lie in providing systems to satisfy the changing demands placed upon them by the users. In the telephone system the user expects what he calls good service, and he expects this service at very low cost. It is the engineer's job to keep this system abreast of the demand. Whether the telephone system will ultimately include television and other methods of communicating between individuals remains to be seen. Demands for long-distance communication increase, and there is pressure to reduce the cost.

Transportation, particularly in the neighborhoods of very large cities, poses major problems. Commuter travel, originally primarily on railroads, has shifted to automobiles. Concurrently the quality and frequency of railroad service have deteriorated. Costs have increased, and the commuter has been reluctant to pay these costs. Thus a spiral of reduced service and rising prices has developed. As the automobile has been brought into service for commuter transportation, the necessity for freeways or expressways has developed, and the impossibility of solving the problem in this manner is becoming apparent. Not only may it be practically impossible to provide enough lanes of transportation; it is questionable that the parking problem can be solved.

The general problem of transportation involving air, rail, and automobile requires serious attention if there is to be proper integration of these various means of transportation. Short hauls by jet aircraft, involving a rapid rise to an elevation and immediate descent because of the proximity of the destination, seems to be out of phase with the abandonment of railroads serving cities two to three hundred miles apart. Transportation of individuals over distances of several hundred miles by automobile is not necessarily the best method when the railroads, which are gradually giving up passenger transportation, might do the job better. One envisions an engineering attack on this problem, in order to integrate the transportation facilities of at least a country, and hopefully of a continent, in a system that will optimize the movement of people and goods with respect to acceptable criteria.

During the next century the provision of sufficient food for the expanding population throughout the world will raise problems demanding the best engineering talent obtainable. If the population does not increase, the food can be supplied. But if the population continues to grow, as it promises to do, it is not now apparent how all the people can be fed without drastic revisions in methods. This poses an engineering problem of staggering complexity and difficulty.

The exhaustion of our natural resources proceeds at a pace that may well tax our ingenuity to provide substitutes or find new sources. Fossil fuels will be exhausted within the foreseeable future. Iron ore is disappearing rapidly, and other basic materials, such as copper and manganese, will be in short supply within a century or two. The solution of these problems does not lie in the simple design of a new machine or two. Rather, it calls for the design of an entire system directed toward the use of available resources for the production of necessary items and a search for new sources of scarce materials to supply the needs of man in the future.

1.7. Education of the Engineer

The history of American engineering education is unique among professional-educational programs. Prior to the Second World War, the education of the engineer was encompassed in four-year curricula, leading to a bachelor's degree in a specialized field of engineering. This contrasted sharply with the educational programs of the other professions, notably medicine and law, in which the emphasis has been on the acquisition of a bachelor of arts degree before entering upon the program leading to a professional degree.

Engineering education is unique in another respect. Education for the profession has been controlled, almost exclusively, by the educators, in contrast with the control of medical education by the practitioners of the art. The American Society for Engineering Education, formerly called the Society for the Promotion of Engineering Education, has been active for well over half a century in formulating the policy that governs American engineering education.

At regular 10-year intervals comprehensive studies of engineering education in the United States have been made. Reports of these studies recommended changes that have profoundly influenced engineering curricula. The Wickenden report[1] in the late 1920s and the Grinter report[2] in 1955 were followed by rapid evolution in engineering education.

The pre-World War II pattern led to a bachelor's degree providing professional status. This program emphasized design, notably in mechanical engineering and civil engineering curricula, but the design was in the framework of the then current state of the art. Civil engineers learned to design standard bridges and buildings; mechanical engineers learned to design internal-combustion engines. They relied heavily on information in handbooks. True creativity was not encouraged.

The Wickenden report pointed out the evils of overspecialization, which attained its peak in the late 1920s. Curricula were then offered in essentially every possible subdivision of engineering, many of which no longer exist. For example, aeronautical engineering curricula came into existence and disappeared in one generation. The report pointed also to the need for emphasis on the humanities and social sciences to enhance engineers' appreciation of the impact of technology on society. These subjects had been neglected in favor of mathematics, science, and their applications in the engineering disciplines.

The rapid developments in certain areas during the Second World War, for example, radar and nuclear energy, established the need for a much better understanding of the basic sciences and mathematics and the ability to apply this knowledge in creative design. During this period many physicists holding doctor's degrees worked as engineers. They were well versed in nuclear science and basic electrical science, and they were able to apply their knowledge adequately under wartime pressures. But they were not particularly concerned with economy or optimization of design, which are the essence of engineering.

The postwar Grinter report reemphasized the need for greater attention to the humanities and social sciences in engineering educa-

---

[1] Report of the Investigation of Enginering Education, vols. I and II, Society for the Promotion of Engineering Education, 1934.

[2] Report on Evaluation of Engineering Education, *J. Eng. Educ.*, vol. 46, no. 1, pp. 25–60, September, 1955.

tion. It also urged greater emphasis on science and mathematics and on the subjects it defined as the engineering sciences, that is, the applied sciences that form the basis of all engineering analysis. Following this report, there began to be established undergraduate curricula in what is variously called engineering science, science engineering, and the like. This was accompanied by graduate programs concentrating on engineering science and analysis, to the exclusion of design. In the 1960s, as a result of the Grinter report and the pressures of postwar industrial, aerospace, and military developments, approximately one-fourth of the engineers with a bachelor's degree obtain a master's degree and approximately one-eighth of that group go on to a doctor's degree.

The emphasis on humanities and the social sciences and on engineering science increased to such an extent that there is now a very strong feeling in engineering-education circles that the pendulum has swung too far and that at both undergraduate and graduate levels there must be a new emphasis on creative engineering design, in order to train professional engineers who can create the systems of the future. The assumption that creative design will come spontaneously from engineers soundly educated in the engineering sciences is no longer accepted as a truism.

New curricula leading to the master of engineering and doctor of engineering degrees have recently been established, and the number of colleges and universities granting these degrees will increase in number to supply the demand for creative professional engineers.

Engineers educated to the doctorate level in both areas—engineering science and creative design—are needed. However, the overall responsibility for the design of a system or device is that of the professional engineer. The engineer who prefers to work in applied science and wishes to do engineering research should secure a doctorate, usually the Ph.D. degree in engineering, and seek his employment in the field of applied or engineering research. Here the motivation is to satisfy recognized needs for new knowledge.

The engineer who wishes a career in professional creative engineering design is well advised to take a master's degree and a doctor's degree in engineering, with emphasis on design. He must be as well versed as the scientist in the basic sciences and in mathematics, but he needs, in addition, knowledge of the fields of economics, social science, and the humanities and, above all, an appreciation of human needs and the influence of engineering design on the technology and the civilization of his day.

Problems

1.1. It is becoming difficult to ensure an adequate supply of water for large cities. Several cities, notably New York City and Los Angeles, are securing their supplies from very distant sources. The availability of these distant supplies is not assured for the future. The decision of the Supreme Court that California can have less water from the Colorado River than had been expected, and that Arizona can have more, will have important effects on the water supply for these two states. New York City is finding that the demand for water by other cities reduces the possibility of extending very much further the range from which its supply is drawn. Suggest solutions for the water-supply problems of Los Angeles and of New York City, assuming that the populations will increase during the next 100 years at a rate comparable to the current rate. Take into consideration the climate of the two areas and make reasonable assumptions concerning the developments in technology of the next century.

1.2. The pollution of the atmosphere is progressing rapidly and, in the vicinity of large cities, is becoming a serious problem. Suggest solutions of this problem, taking into consideration the fact that air pollution is produced by industrial processes and automobiles. Give due thought to human reactions to suggested solutions; also consider carefully the fact that Los Angeles has not found it absolutely necessary to solve the problem, although the condition of the air is frequently very objectionable.

1.3. The city of Chicago appears to be in a period of transition from the use of railroads to the use of automobiles for commuter transportation. Several of the railroads are decreasing their commuter service and at least one has given up entirely. High-speed highways are being built to connect the suburbs with the downtown area. Suggest a method of integrating the transportation system of Chicago so that full advantage will be taken of all available means of transporting commuters to the downtown section of the city.

1.4. Suggest a solution of our food-supply problem, which includes an increasing rate of food production, a decreasing number of persons required on the farm to produce food, growing food surpluses, and food shortages in certain areas of the world. Confine your attention to the production of food in the United States, suggesting a plan that would develop a balance between our production and our requirements by the year 2000.

1.5. It is probable that our supply of iron ore will be exhausted within the foreseeable future. Suggest a possible solution of the problem, assuming that we shall be unable to import adequate supplies from abroad.

References

Gosling, W.: "The Design of Engineering Systems," pp. 205–206, John Wiley & Sons, Inc., New York, 1962.

Hall, Arthur D.: "A Methodology for Systems Engineering," pp. 23–84, D. Van Nostrand Company, Inc., Princeton, N.J., 1962.

Report of the Investigation of Engineering Education, vols. I and II, Society for the Promotion of Engineering Education, 1934.

Report on Evaluation of Engineering Education, *J. Eng. Educ.,* vol. 46, no. 1, pp. 25–60, September, 1955.

System Design

2.1. Introduction It was pointed out in Chap. 1 that the engineer responsible for the design of a system must have a broad background, great capabilities for organization, willingness to assume responsibility, and the drive to see a project through to completion. This chapter and those that follow treat the problems confronting the engineer in system synthesis and analysis. Since the design of a large system requires the efforts of many people, it cannot be a one-man effort; rather, there must be a well-organized team prepared to do the job.

System engineering is a new concept. Practitioners of the art have not had an opportunity to organize and agree upon the definitions and methods inherent in the procedures of creative design. In this chapter an attempt is made to synthesize the elements of a minimum framework on which can be built an organization and a method of creative system engineering. These methods and organizational requirements are illustrated by an example.

2.2. Organization of System Design

The engineer must proceed in an orderly fashion in the design of a system. Table 2.1 lists the first four of the steps that were out-

Table 2.1

Function	Manpower, %	Time, %
Statement of needs and objectives	5	10
Feasibility and preliminary design	20	25
Development	40	40
Prototype construction and evaluation	35	25
	100	100

lined in Sec. 1.5, along with the manpower requirements and time schedule.   These two items are given as percentages of the total time required.   The fifth step must be treated as an independent item.

The first step is the statement of needs and objectives.   This requires about 5 per cent of the total expenditure of manpower and perhaps 10 per cent of the total time devoted to the first four steps of the project.   The feasibility study and preliminary design require about 20 per cent of the manpower and 25 per cent of the total time.   Development, which includes research, design, and modeling, requires about 40 per cent of both manpower and time. The construction of the prototype and its evaluation and test might require 35 per cent of the manpower and 25 per cent of the time. The fifth step—final design, construction, and field observation— varies so widely that it would be unrealistic to attempt to define it in terms of the first four steps.   These figures are crude estimates and can be only approximate from project to project.   They represent a synthesis of the opinions and considerable experience of a number of writers on the subject and are presented to establish orders of magnitude of the various steps in project work.

2.3.   Distinguishing Features of a System

Before proceeding to an example of a system design we shall consider the features that distinguish the design of a system from the design of a component.   Since the illustration to be used later will be a freeway system, the distinction between a freeway system and a complex of highways and streets is made now.

An area traversed by ordinary highways and streets, with the customary traffic-control signs and signals, provides for the movement of traffic in an orderly manner but with no assurance that the traffic flow has been optimized in any sense. An expressway or freeway, incorporating the concept of the division of traffic moving in opposite directions and the elimination of cross traffic, constitutes a component of a freeway system. This element improves the flow of traffic and increases safety but gives only minimum control over the rate of traffic flow. It fixes directions, basically, and not rate of flow, except insofar as speed limits are effective in doing so. If congestion occurs, there is no built-in provision to improve matters at a particular time and place.

The difference between the control afforded by the expressway and the ordinary highway is further illustrated in Fig. 2-1. An intersection at grade of a four-lane highway and a two-lane highway is shown. Traffic is moving on the four-lane highway and is stopped on the two-lane highway and from the two-lane highway onto the main highway. Left turns from the main road onto the two-lane highway must be provided for by signals; this is one of the most difficult aspects of control of traffic at an intersection without separation of traffic flow. The expressway, with separation of traffic in the two directions and separation of the on and off traffic, effects a significant degree of control without the use of traffic lights. This is analogous to the control that can be obtained in an electric circuit, such as that shown in Fig. 2.2, by designing the circuitry and the size of the conduits to provide for the direction and magnitude of the current.

Figure 2.2 illustrates the analogy between conductors carrying

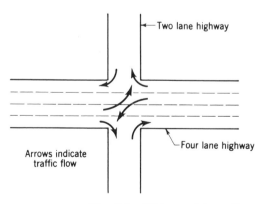

Fig. 2.1   Highway intersection.

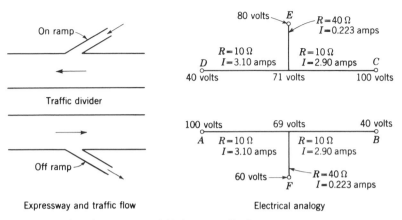

Fig. 2.2 Electrical analog of highway traffic flow.

electric currents and a four-lane expressway with on and off ramps and separated traffic flow. The traffic flow proceeds from *A* to *B* on the two-lane portion of the expressway designed for flow in that direction. The off ramp to the point *F* is a single-lane highway. Similarly, on the other side of the highway, traffic flows from *C* to *D*, and there is an on-coming single-lane ramp from *E*. In the electrical analogy, there are conductors extending from *A* to *B*, with a total 20-ohm resistance, and a conductor, representing the off ramp *F*, with a total 40-ohm resistance. Potentials at the points *A*, *F*, and *B* are 100, 80, and 40 volts, respectively. Current flows from *A* toward *B* and *F*; the greatest flow is on the main line, *A* to *B*, with a much lesser flow toward *F*. Similarly, in the conductor *CD*, flow is from right to left, since the potential is 100 at the right end and 40 at the left. The resistances are similar to those in the other section, and flow occurs from *E* into the main line *CD*, since the potential at *E* is 80 and that at the midpoint is 71.

The amount of current flowing in each element of the electrical system is precisely determined and is predicted by the laws relating voltage, current, and resistance. These voltages and currents are shown in Fig. 2.2. In the case of the highway, the rate at which traffic flows depends on speed limits and the driving habits of the vehicle operators. There is a fair analogy, however, between current and traffic flow, in that the traffic-flow capacity of a two-lane highway with a normal speed limit is not subject to very wide variations under ordinary driving conditions. The restriction imposed by

Fig. 2.3   Block diagram of traffic flow.

single-lane off ramps is similar to that of a high-resistance link in the electric circuit, such as the 40-ohm branches to points *E* and *F*. Traffic stops flowing on an off ramp if the demand for its use exceeds the capacity, which is fixed by its width and by the conditions at the ramp's intersection with some other portion of the highway system. If equations could be written to give relationships between the rate of traffic flow, the width of the highway, and other conditions, it would be possible to analyze the traffic-flow problem in much the same way as the electrical-flow problem of Fig. 2.2. The analogy is useful in pointing out that the two situations have many features in common but that traffic flow is a much more difficult problem than electrical flow.

A section of an expressway may be described by Fig. 2.3. The box labeled highway could be either a component of a system or a whole system. Here it represents the section *A, B, C, D, E, F,* as shown in Fig. 2.2. This is a section of highway into which and out of which vehicles move. The incoming vehicles represent an input—vehicles demanding a means of transportation from one point to another. If this demand exceeds the highway's capacity, the number of vehicles going out is less than those coming in and traffic will back up along the highway. No further control is designed into the system; hence it would not respond to excessive demands and adapt to changing situations.

A traffic-flow problem with greater complexity than the simple intersection shown in Fig. 2.1 can be solved by a freeway system. This is illustrated in a highly idealized example in the following section.

2.4.   Example of a Preliminary Design: A Freeway System

Figure 2.4 shows the general layout of a metropolitan area with a serious traffic problem. The area is 30 miles square and consists of a central business district 2 miles square surrounded by a mixed business-residential section 8 by 6 miles. Each rectangular-

Table 2.2

	Population		
	Urban	*Suburban*	*Total*
1963	10^6	4×10^5	1.4×10^6
1970	1.2×10^6	7×10^5	1.9×10^6
1980	1.6×10^6	1.2×10^6	2.8×10^6

shaped business district is centered in the 30 by 30-mile square, the
outer portions of which are a suburban residential area. The population of this area in 1963 and the estimated populations in 1970
and 1980 are shown in Table 2.2. The extremely bad current
traffic flow indicates a serious need for an improvement in transportation, either by a rapid-transit system or a freeway system.
It is assumed that a study, which would be, in itself, one of extreme complexity, has shown that a freeway system is preferable.

Currently, the east-west highway is filled to capacity inbound

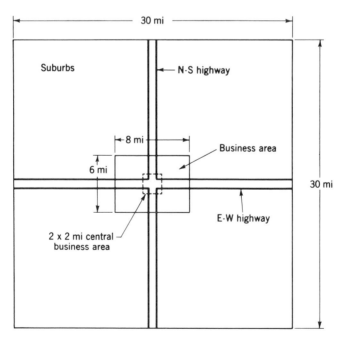

Fig. 2.4 Map of a metropolitan area.

between the hours of 8 and 9:30 A.M. and outbound between 5 and 7 P.M., as is the north-south highway at the same times. Flow is at the rate of 80 cars per minute on each of the four inbound highways. Cars move at an average rate of 10 to 12 mph in the urban sections; in the suburban areas they are able to travel between 30 and 40 mph but slow down as they approach the urban boundaries. It requires 70 min to make the journey from the outer edges of the suburban areas to the downtown center at the peak of the rush hour.

Preliminary studies have been made in order to supply data for a feasibility study, to determine the desirability of building a freeway system and, indeed, the practicability of building it. These studies have resulted in the following crude data.

Traffic appears to originate approximately uniformly throughout the suburban area at the rate of 50 cars per square mile in the period between 7 and 8:30 A.M. It originates uniformly in the business district between 4:30 and 6:00 P.M. at the rate of 800 cars per square mile.

The distribution of the incoming traffic in the business area during the morning rush hour is found, again, to be roughly uniform throughout the 48-square-mile area; in the evening, distribution is uniform throughout the suburban area.

For a freeway system to be considered satisfactory, it has been established that the maximum driving time from the outskirts of the suburban area should not exceed 45 min. This represents a composite of approximately 4 or 5 miles on feeder highway, 20 miles on the freeway, and about a mile in the downtown section. This might be broken down in terms of time as 12 min on the feeders, 25 min on the freeway, and 8 min in the downtown section, including time for parking.

These data indicate the need for a total capacity of approximately 40,000 cars in a 90-min period during both the morning and the evening rush hours, and there should be a peak potential of 10,000 cars per hour per freeway if four freeways to the downtown section are contemplated. Provisions should be made for expansion to the conditions of 1980 with no great additional cost, and design should be in terms of 1970 rather than 1963 if one is to be realistic in terms of the time required to build the system.

At this point, it is well to observe that, before any analysis directed toward a determination of cost, freeway capacities, and suitability can begin, a decision concerning a first approach to the design must be made. It is not necessary to use formal methods to get a good design. Analysis provides the information to ensure optimization by comparison of various designs. But it is impossible to analyze a freeway system until one has a freeway system, on paper, at least. At hand now, in this problem, are only the data set forth above and the material shown in Fig. 2.4.

In order to have some concrete plan with which to work, the system depicted in Fig. 2.5 is suggested. Here are shown diagonal freeways extending from the four corners of the square area, which is 30 miles on each side, to the downtown central section. The two diagonal freeways are designed to cross each other at this point, with a complete interchange between them. Outside the urban section there would be two lanes in each direction, and within the urban area three lanes in each direction, with on and off ramps at locations yet to be determined. The preliminary sketch suggests four four-lane freeways converging toward the urban section, approximately 16 miles long in each case. Within the urban area

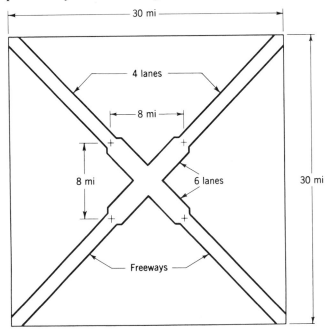

Fig. 2.5   Freeway system.

the highways would be six-lane, each about 5 miles in length from the corner of the rectangle to the center of the downtown section. Tables 2.3 and 2.4 give a summary of unit costs in terms of the cost of construction of the freeway and the cost of land needed for right-of-way.

With this suggested freeway system on paper, it is possible to analyze its performance and determine if it is adequate for the established demands.

The 1963 data indicate that in the morning hours 444 vehicles per minute originate in the suburban area. This is equivalent to 111 per minute on each branch of the freeways. These vehicles are assumed to originate uniformly across the area. If it is assumed that this traffic can move at the rate of 60 mph, with a space of 100 ft between cars, the capacity of a single lane is 88/100 car per second, or approximately 55 cars per minute. With 111 cars originating per minute on each branch, two lanes inbound during the morning rush hour are required. In the afternoon, vehicles would enter the freeway at the same rate, and two lanes again would be needed for the outbound traffic.

However, consideration must be given to the on and off ramps, to provide for the traffic entering and leaving the freeway at the rush

Table 2.3

Cost of land		
Central business section	4 sq miles	3×10^5 per acre
Outer business section	44 sq miles	6×10^4 per acre
Suburban area	852 sq miles	2×10^4 per acre

Table 2.4

Freeway construction costs	
Suburban four-lane	$300,000 per mile
Urban six-lane	$700,000 per mile
Width of right-of-way	
Suburban	250 ft
Urban	150 ft

hours.   In the area with but two lanes, cars cannot enter the freeway at a rate much exceeding 10 cars per minute.   Under these
circumstances, at least 11 on ramps would be necessary on each of
the four freeways.   This suggests a spacing of about $1\frac{1}{3}$ miles
between the on ramps in the suburban area.   Similarly, in the
downtown area, if 12 on ramps were required for the afternoon
traffic, the spacing must be closer, since there are only 5 miles of
downtown freeway on each of the four branches.   Spacing of the on
ramps downtown, then, would be at approximately $\frac{1}{2}$-mile intervals.
If we postulate that off traffic moves at the same rate as on traffic, the
same spacing would be needed for off ramps as is required for on
ramps.   The need for the third lane in the downtown section can be
established readily, since at the time of the inbound rush in the
morning the third lane would be essentially incapacitated by the
frequency of the off ramps and the slower traffic moving off.   It
would be necessary, then, to have two lanes for through traffic and
one lane for the off traffic throughout the downtown section.

   This is a very crude analysis of the situation and is useful only
in a preliminary feasibility study.   It would not be successful in
establishing the actual flow conditions.   A more detailed analysis of
the flow situation is required and calls for much better data on the
rate of flow through on and off ramps in the downtown section, as
well as in a suburban section.   In Tables 2.5 and 2.6, the data for

---

Table 2.5

Length of four-lane suburban freeways is 64 miles.
Length of six-lane urban freeways is 20 miles, 14 miles in outer business area,
   6 miles in central area.

Areas required per mile of freeway:
$$\text{Urban} = \frac{5{,}280 \times 150}{43{,}560} = 17.8 \text{ acres/mile}$$

$$\text{Suburban} = \frac{5{,}280 \times 250}{43{,}560} = 30.2 \text{ acres/mile}$$

Land values:

Central urban =	4 sq miles = 2,560	acres @ 3×10^5 =		768×10^6
Outer urban =	44 sq miles = 28,160	acres @ 6×10^4 =		$1{,}690 \times 10^6$
Suburban =	852 sq miles = 546,000	acres @ 2×10^4 =		$10{,}920 \times 10^6$
				$\$13{,}378 \times 10^6$

Table 2.6

	Miles of freeway	Acres of land	Cost of land	Cost of construction	Total cost
			Costs of 1963 design		
Location					
Central urban	6	107	32.1×10^6	4.2×10^6	36.3×10^6
Outer urban	14	249	14.9×10^6	9.8×10^6	24.7
Suburban	64	1,930	38.6×10^6	19.2×10^6	57.8
Total	84	2,286	85.6×10^6	33.2×10^6	118.8×10^6
Unit costs per freeway	21	572	21.4×10^6	8.3×10^6	29.7×10^6
Annual cost, four freeways					11.9×10^6
Annual cost per freeway					3.0×10^6
Number vehicles					350,000
Annual cost per vehicle					34.00
Annual cost per person					8.50
Annual cost per dollar land value					0.00089

Costs of 1970 design

Increased in ratio of suburban population: $\frac{7}{4} \times$ 1963 design

Location	Total cost
Central urban	63.5×10^6
Outer urban	43.2
Suburban	101.0
Total	207.7×10^6
Number vehicles	475,000
Annual cost total	20.77×10^6
Per vehicle	43.80
Per person	10.90
Per dollar land value*	0.00155

Costs of 1980 design

Increased in ratio of population: $1\frac{2}{4} = 3 \times$ 1963 design

Location	Total cost
Central urban	108.9×10^6
Outer urban	74.1
Suburban	173.4
Total	356.4×10^6
Number vehicles	700,000
Annual cost total	35.64×10^6
Per vehicle	50.90
Per person	12.30
Per dollar land value*	0.00266

Table 2.6 *(Continued)*

	Number of cars	Parking space *Area, acres*	*Cost*
1963	40,000	266	9.32×10^6
1970	70,000	467	16.30×10^6
1980	120,000	800	27.96×10^6

Space per car: 300 sq ft, or 150 cars per acre
Downtown space costs: $300,000 per acre
Improvement cost: $50,000 per acre

Hence, cost per car $= \dfrac{350,000}{150} = \$2,330$ per car

Annual cost per car $= \$233.00$

* 1963 land values.

1963, 1970, and 1980 are summarized, making the assumption that the number of vehicles will increase directly in proportion to the suburban population and that land values will not increase.

Several pertinent facts are revealed by this tabulation and explain to a considerable extent the reasons for expansion of freeway systems and the concern for the future of urban areas. First, the costs of the freeway per vehicle, per person, and per dollar of land value are very reasonable. Thus extension of freeway systems can be sold to the public. Secondly, the area in urban sections devoted to freeways and parking is excessive. The tabulation for 1980 shows a central urban area of 1,121 acres devoted to freeways and parking, assuming all parking is concentrated in the central section; this is almost 2 square miles or 50 per cent of the total central urban area.

A 1980 cost of $50 per vehicle per year for the freeways appears low and salable. If this is converted to cost per gallon of gasoline, as it might well be in the form of a gasoline tax, the amount can be established by noting that the average car would use between 500 and 1,000 gal per year. If $50 is raised in tax on 1,000 gal, the tax is 5 cents per gallon. Expressed in these terms, the cost appears higher than otherwise and indicates that there might be some difficulty in financing the project. The estimates for 1963 show a per-vehicle cost of $34, or a gasoline tax of 3.4 cents per gallon.

Under these circumstances there would be heavy pressure to keep the cost of freeways low, and the design problem would entail a considerable effort to optimize the design in terms of freeway capacity per dollar of cost.

2.5. Organization for Design

Detailed design of this freeway system would follow a decision that feasibility had been established. If the decision were against continuance, a new proposal might be made or the scheme would be dropped.

Assuming that feasibility has been established, we consider now the steps that might be followed. Clearly a single pattern for freeways is not sufficient basis for a conclusive study. Furthermore, data on origin and destinations of traffic are sketchy at best. Details of costs for various freeway widths and types are needed. In consideration of these apparent needs and others that will develop in such a project, an organization and plan of action would be somewhat as follows:

Project Outline
1. Establish basic data
   a. Traffic densities
   b. Land costs
   c. Construction costs
   d. Construction time requirements
   e. Criteria for evaluation of system performance
2. Make preliminary freeway-system layouts
   a. Location of freeways
   b. Number of lanes
   c. Location of ramps
   d. Location of interchanges
3. Devise mathematical models of systems
   a. Physical layout
   b. Traffic flow
4. Analyze performance by model
   a. Normal traffic
   b. Peak traffic
   c. Emergency conditions

5. Compare performance of various systems
    a. Using established criteria
    b. Using other criteria
6. Redesign and evaluate
7. Make final design
    a. System characteristics
    b. Construction details
    c. Right-of-way acquisition
    d. Construction schedule
    e. Costs

To carry out a project of this scope and magnitude, an organization along the lines shown in Fig. 2.6 might be used. The overall responsibility lies with the project engineer who must coordinate the activities of the heads of the analytical and design groups.

The chronology of the prosecution of the work would depend, to a large extent, upon the availability of information and manpower and the acceptability of designs as they are made. For example, preliminary freeway layouts can be made immediately by the system synthesis group. These are given to the mathematical analysts who devise the model and predict performance. At the same time, the research and information group can gather the data needed for all phases of the project. The highway and structural design group can proceed with basic highway, bridge, and interchange designs before final locations are established.

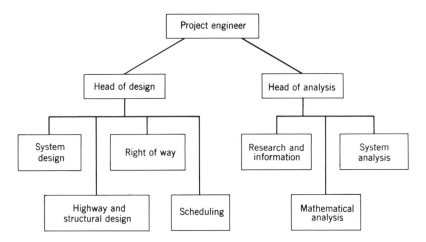

Fig. 2.6   Organization chart for freeway project.

As system analysis produces evaluations of various proposals, decisions are made, and finally a system is selected. Activity in analysis subsides, and design proceeds more rapidly. However, analysis will be necessary as inevitable changes dictated by right-of-way, aesthetic, or political considerations are made.

Ultimately, drawings become available, land acquisition gets under way, and finally construction begins. After the system is in use, system analysis and evaluation of the prototype are undertaken to establish adequacy and lay the groundwork for expansion or revision.

The organization of Fig. 2.6 would require the services of persons with many different backgrounds. In analysis, library search calls for one group of talents. Mathematical analysis requires the services of applied mathematicians and engineers. Systems analysis uses a similar type of person with background in system rather than straightforward mathematical analysis.

In the design section, system designers are engineers with a creative rather than analytical flair. Highway and structural designers are engineers with civil and structural engineering backgrounds. Scheduling calls for engineers with production engineering experience. The right-of-way group will include members with legal training.

The section heads will generally be engineers with 5 to 15 years experience and the project engineer one with 10 or more years in the highway field.

2.6. Optimizing the Design

The feasibility study and preliminary design suggested by the freeway problem of Sec. 2.4 are an example, at a very elementary level, of the first steps that must be taken in making decisions concerning the desirability of undertaking the design of a system. Nothing was said in this elementary study about the relative merits of various solutions that might be suggested. Minimum criteria were established for driving time, speeds, and the like, but after considering the possibility of four links in the freeway system, all directed toward the center of the city, nothing further was done to examine a different synthesis that might handle the traffic more expeditiously.

With the suggested system of four diagonal sections of freeway, it was shown that it might be possible to handle the traffic at a cost that could be considered reasonable in the foreseeable future. After a design study has proceeded to this point, other methods of solving the problem should be considered, with estimates of their workability and cost, and the several solutions compared to determine the one deserving of further study.

Such a process is a step toward optimization of the design in terms of the stated criteria by which it will be judged. The essence of the concept of optimization is that there is available some criterion judged to be suitable for establishing the value of a solution to a problem.

The terms judgment, value, and optimization all directly imply that a value system is available. For example, in the case of the freeway system, one criterion for judging the merit of a solution is the quantity of traffic that can be carried by the system. This was recognized in deciding on the number of ramps and the number of lanes required. Further detailed studies would reveal that there may be better ways of locating ramps and selecting the number of lanes of traffic than the simple methods used in the preliminary feasibility study above. More data are necessary to make these detailed studies. However, in order to draw a conclusion concerning the relative merits of various suggestions, first a criterion must be selected: for example, the quantity of traffic that can be handled by a given system in a particular period of time. This choice of a criterion requires judgment on the part of the designer. The ultimate solution is fixed, to a considerable extent, by the selection of a criterion.

It must be kept in mind that, after the criterion has been decided upon, the course is quite well determined; all that one can hope to do in the detail of the design is to optimize the situation with respect to the criterion already selected. Choice of a different criterion might have much more effect on the final design than anything that can be done in refinement of the design itself.

Problems

In each of the following problems, consider the feasibility of carrying out the suggested solution.

2.1. Reprocess the sewage of a large city and return the purified water to the water mains to supplement the city's inadequate supply of fresh water. Be sure to consider the problem of selling this concept to the citizens.

2.2. Use alcohol as an automobile fuel to reduce the smog problem in large cities. Assume that a significant reduction in the production of smog will be accomplished by using alcohol rather than gasoline as the fuel and that the operation of automobiles with alcohol is satisfactory. Consider the impact on the petroleum industry and the source of supply of raw material for the manufacture of alcohol.

2.3. Construct and operate a high-speed railroad, connecting the cities of Washington, New York, and Boston. Assume that it will be possible to build such a railroad on existing rights-of-way, with some modifications of alignment, and that average speeds of 120 mph can be maintained. Such a railroad now operates in Japan and will maintain an average speed of 100 mph, with peaks of over 120. Consider the competition of airlines and automobiles. The distances are approximately: Washington to New York, 220 miles; New York to Boston, 210 miles. Airplanes fly the distance from Washington to New York, or from New York to Boston, in less than an hour, but travel to and from the airports requires about the same amount of time. Railroads make either of these runs in something over 3 hr and slightly less than 4 hr. The major traffic is Washington to New York, or New York to Boston, or the reverse, with a minor amount covering the full distance, Washington to Boston.

2.4. Operate a public transportation system without charging fare. This could be a subway system, such as that of New York City; a bus system operating on expressways; or commuter trains on established railroads. Consider the possible source of revenue to support such a system and public reaction to the raising of funds in the suggested manner, as well as the public reaction to a free, or apparently free, transportation system.

References
Asimow, Morris: "Introduction to Design," pp. 24–33, Prentice-Hall, Inc., Englewood Cliffs, N.J., 1962.

Doebelin, E. O.: "Dynamic Analysis and Feedback Control," pp. 16–24, 173–192, McGraw-Hill Book Company, New York, 1962.

Hall, Arthur D.: "A Methodology for Systems Engineering," pp. 85–145, D. Van Nostrand Company, Inc., Princeton, N.J., 1962.

Lynch, W. A., and J. G. Truxal: "Introductory System Analysis," pp. 1–11, 65–121, 135–191, McGraw-Hill Book Company, New York, 1961.

———— and ————: "Principles of Electronic Instrumentation," McGraw-Hill Book Company, New York, 1962.

Computers

3.1. The Role of Computers in Engineering The engineer has always used mathematics extensively as a tool in his work. The quality of the designs produced depends on the solutions of mathematical problems. He has continually sought more powerful methods and greater accuracy and speed to enhance his ability to predict performance of components and systems.

Traditionally, the engineer and the student of engineering have used the slide rule, which is an analog computer. It was developed in the early seventeenth century and reduced considerably the time required for multiplication, division, and exponentiation in engineering calculations. Its most serious limitation was the accuracy obtainable. In general, three significant figures could be counted upon. In the seventeenth, eighteenth, and part of the nineteenth century, this accuracy was adequate.

Later there was need for higher speed and greater accuracy in calculations. In response to this demand, at the middle of the nineteenth century a number of mechanical calculating machines became available. They were first sold commercially about 1820, and by 1865 approximately 500 had been manufactured.

The availability of computing devices and the increase in

sophistication of the background theory used by the engineer in design went hand in hand, the one inspiring improvements in the other throughout the seventeenth, eighteenth, and nineteenth centuries. At the beginning of the twentieth century, the theoretical background was such that, had there been available high-speed computing devices, much better design would have been possible. The component or system to be designed could have been represented by a mathematical model and its performance predicted with a higher degree of precision than that of the slide rule and desk calculator, with their severe limitations on the speed attainable in carrying out long and tedious analyses.

As a result of this combination of circumstances, the design procedures of the early part of the twentieth century were based upon simplifications necessitated not by the engineering concepts but rather by practical economics. It was not always feasible to carry out the mathematical and computational procedures necessary to analyze thoroughly the structure, device, or system before construction.

As an example, the civil engineer designed bridges that were statically determinate; i.e., the stress in any member can be determined without considering the deformations. He constructed them in such a manner that he could use analysis methods derived from elementary mechanics and requiring only a single set of very elementary computations to determine all the stresses in a rather complex structure. He was aware that economies could be effected if the design took advantage of the greater strength of a structure that is not statically determinate but rather has structural members that sustain bending stresses as well as longitudinal forces.

This situation is illustrated in Fig. 3.1*a*. This shows a load *W* supported by means of a horizontal bar *BC*, which is connected at a vertical wall by means of a pin passing through the bar and a support bolted securely to the wall. The bar *BC* in turn is supported at the end *B* by means of a cable *AB*. The connection at *A* is again a pinned connection to the wall. The significance of pinned connections is that they are incapable of sustaining a twisting effort or moment. As a consequence, the cable *AB* is in tension; that is, it will support a load only in the direction of the line *AB*. The bar *BC* will be compressed by forces at the ends *B* and *C*, respectively. The combination of the tension in the cable *AB* and the compression

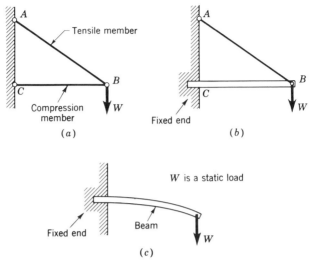

Fig. 3.1 Simple structures.

in the bar *BC* supplies support for the load *W* if the bar and cable are sufficiently strong.

An alternative way of handling this load, which provides greater rigidity, hence under certain circumstances greater economy, is shown in Fig. 3.1*b*. Here the horizontal bar *BC* has been replaced by a beam securely imbedded in the wall at point *C*. It, in turn, is supported at the point *B* by the cable *AB*, which is pin-connected at the point *B*, as before. Added strength is derived from the fact that the beam, or bar *BC*, is imbedded in the wall at *C* and will resist twisting moments exerted on it. For example, if the cable *AB* were removed, the beam *BC* would still support the load *W*, the moment of which is the weight *W* multiplied by the distance *BC*. It would bend downward at the outer end and assume a shape somewhat as shown in Fig. 3.1*c*. The presence of the cable *AB* serves to reduce the distance that the point *B* moves downward. At the same time, the added rigidity of the bar at point *C*, given by its imbedment in the wall, reduces the tension produced in the cable *AB,* since it tends to move down a much lesser amount at point *B*. The interaction of the cable and bending strength of the beam contributes to economy.

Methods have been developed to analyze structures of a very complex nature, and the advent of reinforced concrete and welded steel supplied the engineer with techniques that made possible more economical structural design.   With these techniques a bridge could be constructed in which all joints, such as those shown in Fig. 3.1*b*, could be solid welded joints or, in the case of a reinforced-concrete structure, continuously poured.   However, a welded-steel structure or a reinforced-concrete structure with continuous joints, as described here, presents very real difficulties in calculating the stresses and moments in its various parts.   In principle, the theory of elasticity provided the basic concepts to solve most problems in structural design, but so great an expenditure of time was required that it was not possible to justify the savings that might be effected except in certain special cases, in which solutions could be obtained and extended to more complex situations by rule of thumb.

In the early 1930s, Prof. Hardy Cross, at the University of Illinois, proposed a procedure[1] for analyzing continuous steel or concrete structures with very much less engineering effort.   This method of analysis is one of successive approximations, which can yield results of whatever degree of accuracy may be desired.   A large number of structural engineers became expert in the use of this method, which was applied widely in structural design throughout the United States.

The Hardy Cross method of moment distribution continued in use until the advent of the high-speed digital electronic computer in the early 1950s.   The need for the method then disappeared almost overnight, since the equations describing a structure could be solved in a very short period of time and much more exactly than had been possible with Professor Cross's method of successive approximations.   Many engineers, expert in this particular technique, suddenly found a greatly reduced demand for their services.

This development in structural engineering was paralleled elsewhere during the same period of time.   In structural, mechanical, and electrical engineering, the need for consideration of the dynamics of systems developed rapidly.   Structural engineering received a stern reminder of this in the failure of the Tacoma Narrows Bridge.   This catastrophe accentuated the need for design that incorporated consideration of the dynamics of a bridge as well as its performance under static loads.   The bridge was designed in conformity with

[1] Hardy Cross, Analysis of Continuous Frames by Distributing Fixed-end Moments, *Trans. ASCE,* vol. 97, pp. 1–156, 1932.

accepted practice at the time, but its design did not provide for the effect of wind loads, which was to generate an oscillatory motion. Concurrently with developments in structural engineering, there arose in both electrical and mechanical technology a great emphasis on automatic control. This is inherently an area wherein dynamic aspects require the use of sophisticated mathematical techniques to predict performance accurately.

The high degree of development of the analog computer and the electronic digital computer shortly after the middle of the twentieth century made possible adoption of methods of great power and sophistication to predict the performance of devices and systems under various operating conditions. Engineers can now usually describe adequately the performance of a particular element in a system by means of a mathematical model that closely represents the behavior of the component or system itself, with lessened need for simplifying assumptions to make the computations more tractable. It is now economical of both time and money to carry out a thorough-going analysis of performance before construction of a physical model or prototype.

3.2.   The Analog Computer

The analog computer, long familiar to the engineer in the form of the slide rule, has evolved into the all-electronic analog computer in common use today. Analog computers, whether mechanical, electrical, or electronic, have one thing in common: They perform their function by measuring quantities and performing operations on these measured quantities. The equation describing the operation of the computer is analogous to that representing the actual physical system.

For example, the slide rule, one of the simplest of the analog computers, is capable of multiplying, dividing, and exponentiating. Its operation depends upon the fact that multiplication can be performed by the addition of logarithms. The following equation represents the process of multiplication in the ordinary sense:

$$y = xz \tag{3.1}$$

Taking the logarithm of each side of this equation gives

$$\log y = \log x + \log z \tag{3.2}$$

The equation, in terms of logarithms, represents the system. The slide rule makes it possible to perform the operation of multiplication by adding lengths that are proportional to the logarithms.

Figure 3.2 shows two scales of a slide rule. Distances on the scales are proportional to the logarithms of the numbers shown. The logarithm of 1 is 0; hence 1 lies at the left end of the scale. The logarithms of 2, 3, 4, etc., have values proportional to the distances from the left end of each scale. In Fig. 3.2, the 1 of the upper scale is placed opposite 2.6 on the lower scale. An indicator is placed at the location of 3.0 on the upper scale, and immediately below this we read 7.8 on the lower scale, the product of 3 and 2.6. The distance proportional to the logarithm of 2.6 is added to the distance proportional to the logarithm of 3.0, giving a sum proportional to the logarithm of 7.8. The process of division is simply the inverse of multiplication; hence the slide rule is used to perform operations in division as follows: Referring again to Fig. 3.2, if 7.8 is to be divided by 3, the 3 is placed immediately opposite the 7.8 on the other scale, and opposite 1.0 is read the quotient 2.6, obtained by dividing 7.8 by 3.0, thus subtracting from the logarithm of 7.8 the logarithm of 3.0 and obtaining the logarithm of 2.6.

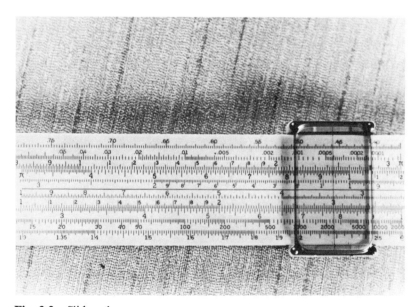

Fig. 3.2   Slide rule.

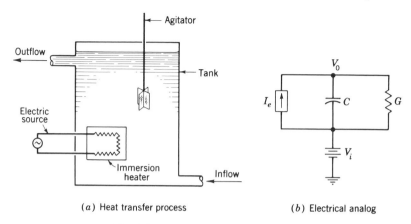

(*a*) Heat transfer process   (*b*) Electrical analog

Fig. 3.3   Heat-transfer process and its electrical analog.

Another example of analog computation is shown in Fig. 3.3, where the electric circuit is the analog of a heat-transfer system. A constant flow of fluid into and out of the tank is maintained. The agitator keeps the temperature uniform throughout the tank. Let Q_i Btu/min of heat be carried in by the fluid at temperature T_i °F. The electric heater supplies heat at the rate Q_e Btu/min. The fluid carries heat out at the rate Q_o Btu/min at the temperature of the tank, T_o °F. The principle of conservation of heat energy states that the difference between the rate of heat inflow and the rate of heat outflow is the rate at which energy is stored in the tank. That is,

$$Q_i + Q_e = Q_o + Q_{\text{stored}} \tag{3.3}$$

From the physical laws of heat transfer, the relationship for the rate of heat storage in the tank is

$$Q_{\text{stored}} = C_T \frac{d(T_o - T_i)}{dt} \tag{3.4}$$

where C_T is the thermal capacity of the tank, in Btu/°F. In addition, a thermal conductance for the process may be defined; it relates the rate of net heat flow out of the tank to the difference between input and output temperatures. Thus,

$$Q_o - Q_i = G_T(T_o - T_i) \tag{3.5}$$

where G_T is the process thermal conductance in Btu/(min)(°F).

Substituting (3.4) and (3.5) into (3.3) yields

$$Q_e = C_T \frac{d(T_o - T_i)}{dt} + G_T(T_o - T_i) \qquad (3.6)$$

The analogy between the heat-transfer process and the electric circuit can be seen clearly by writing the equation corresponding to Kirchhoff's current law at node A.   A node is defined as a junction between circuit elements.   A node has a voltage associated with it, measured with respect to a reference point, commonly a point of zero potential referred to as "ground."   Kirchhoff's current law, which expresses the concept of conservation of charge, states that the algebraic sum of the currents flowing out of a node is equal to zero. The current flowing out through capacitor C is given by $C(d/dt)$ $(V_o - V_i)$.   The current through conductance G, as given by Ohm's law, is $G(V_o - V_i)$.

Ohm's law states that for many resistive materials the voltage is linearly proportional to the current; thus,

$$V \text{ (volts)} = R \text{ (ohms) } I \text{ (amperes)} \qquad \text{Ohm's law}$$

where R is the resistance of the circuit element.   The equation can be written to give I in terms of V:

$$I \text{ (amperes)} = \frac{1}{R \text{ (ohms)}} V \text{ (volts)}$$

where $1/R$ is defined as the conductance G, so that

$$I = GV$$

The units of G are ohms^{-1}, or mhos.   Both resistance R and conductance G are often used in the expression of Ohm's law.   Engineers should be able to use both representations freely.   Conductance G is used throughout this chapter.

The charge stored in a capacitor C is given by

$$Q \text{ (coulombs)} = C \text{ (farads) } V \text{ (volts)}$$

from Coulomb's law.   Differentiating this expression, we have

$$\frac{dQ}{dt} \text{ (coulombs/sec)} = C \text{ (farads) } \frac{dV}{dt} \text{ (volts/sec)}$$

The rate of change of charge is the current I.   Thus, I (amperes) flowing into a capacitor is given by

$$I = C \frac{dV}{dt}$$

The current I is flowing *into* node A from an ideal d-c generator, that is, a generator that supplies constant current I_e regardless of the load placed across its terminals.   Use of Kirchhoff's law, then, gives the equation

$$I_e = C \frac{d(V_o - V_i)}{dt} + G(V_o - V_i) \tag{3.7}$$

Equation (3.7) for the electric circuit is of precisely the same form as Eq. (3.6), where current is analogous to heat flow and voltage analogous to temperature.   Table 3.1 illustrates the analogous quantities.

We see that the electric circuit constitutes a valuable analog computer for analyzing the heat-transfer process.   The effects of varying Q_e, the tank design, input temperature, and other parameters can be quickly ascertained in this computer.   Such a computer is capable of significant savings in time and cost of analysis of many processes and is invaluable in the design of engineering systems.

The expression for the current in the capacitor of the above circuit, $C(dV)/dt$, suggests that electric circuits could be used to carry out mathematical operations such as differentiation and in-

---

**Table 3.1   Electrical Analogs to
Heat-transfer Quantities**

Heat flow Q, Btu/min $\Leftrightarrow$ Current I, amperes
Temperature T, °F $\Leftrightarrow$ Voltage V, volts
Thermal capacity C_T, Btu/°F $\Leftrightarrow$ Capacity C, farads
Thermal conductance G_T, Btu/min °F $\Leftrightarrow$ Conductance G, mhos

---

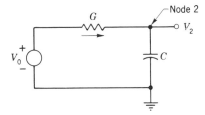

Fig. 3.4   Integrator circuit.

tegration.   Figure 3.4 illustrates such a circuit.   Using Kirchhoff's current law at node 2, we have

$$C\frac{dV_2}{dt} + G(V_2 - V_1) = 0 \tag{3.8}$$

If we integrate the equation, we have

$$V_2(t) = \frac{G}{C}\int_0^t V_1\,dt - \frac{G}{C}\int_0^t V_2\,dt \tag{3.9}$$

Assuming that $V_2(0) = 0$, G/C may be chosen small enough so that V_2 is very nearly equal to $\frac{G}{C}\int_0^t V_1\,dt$.   However, when this is done, the magnitude of V_2 is much less than the magnitude of V_1.   To restore the magnitude of V_2 to a level comparable with V_1, an amplifier would be required, which would be connected across V_2.

Much more efficient use of the amplifier can be made in the circuit shown in Fig. 3.5.   The amplifier, represented by the triangle in the figure, amplifies voltages at its input by the factor $-A$ and draws no current at its input; that is, the current flowing into the

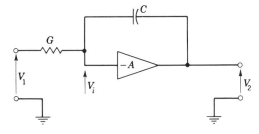

Fig. 3.5   Integrator with operational amplifier.

amplifier from node i is zero. Writing Kirchhoff's current law at node i, we have

$$G(V_i - V_1) + C \frac{d}{dt} (V_i - V_2) = 0 \qquad (3.10)$$

The amplifier forces V_2 to be $-AV_i$, or

$$V_i = - \frac{V_2}{A} \qquad (3.11)$$

Substituting from (3.11) into (3.10) gives

$$G \left(- \frac{V_2}{A} - V_1 \right) = C \frac{d}{dt} \left(V_2 - \frac{V_2}{A} \right) \qquad (3.12)$$

Now as A, the amplifier gain, is made extremely large, the term V_2/A becomes very small, so that (3.12) becomes

$$-GV_1 = C \frac{d}{dt} V_2 \qquad (3.13)$$

Integrating, we have

$$V_2(t) = - \frac{G}{C} \int_0^t V_1 \, dt \qquad (3.14)$$

Assuming $V_2(0) = 0$, the advantage of the above circuit over the integrator of Fig. 3.4 is that, as long as the gain A is high, the circuit performance is relatively insensitive to changes in A and, also, the parameters C and G may be chosen without regard to minimizing the error term $(G/C) \int_0^t V_2 \, dt$ of Eq. (3.9). Thus, the integrator of Fig. 3.5, using the amplifier, is far superior to the integrator of Fig. 3.4.

The analog-computer circuit of Fig. 3.5, which is capable of performing a mathematical *operation* such as integration, has been called an *operational* amplifier. Another example of an operational amplifier is shown in Fig. 3.6. In this case, the operations performed are multiplying V_2 and V_1 by constants and summing the results. Again, the key to understanding the circuit is provided by writing

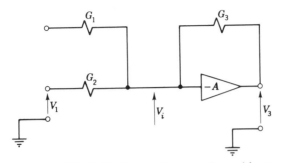

Fig. 3.6 Multiplication and integration with operational amplifier.

Kirchhoff's current law at node i.   We have

$$G_1(V_i - V_1) - G_2(V_i - V_2) + G_3(V_i - V_3) = 0 \qquad (3.15)$$

and the amplifier forcing the relationship

$$V_i = -\frac{V_3}{A} \qquad (3.16)$$

Substituting from (3.16) into (3.15) gives

$$G_1\left(\frac{V_3}{A} - V_1\right) + G_2\left(\frac{V_3}{A} - V_2\right) = G_3\left(V_3 - \frac{V_3}{A}\right) \qquad (3.17)$$

In the limit, as $A \to \infty$, Eq. (3.17) becomes

$$V_3 = \frac{G_1}{G_3} V_1 + \frac{G_2}{G_3} V_2 \qquad (3.18)$$

where V_1 and V_2 are multiplied by constants and summed as anticipated above.

The differential equation

$$\frac{d^2y}{dt^2} + \frac{dy}{dt} - y = x(t) \qquad (3.19)$$

can be rewritten as follows:

$$\frac{d^2y}{dt^2} = x(t) + y - \frac{dy}{dt} \qquad (3.20)$$

At the left end of Fig. 3.4 x, y, and dy/dt are shown as voltages in the analog-computer circuit. These are fed into the first operational amplifier, where they are summed and integrated to produce (dy/dt). This quantity is fed into the second operational amplifier, which integrates it to obtain y. It should be noted that quantities (dy/dt) and y are fed back to the first portion of the circuit from the junctions at which they are generated. This analog-computer circuit produces an output voltage y, which is a function of t and is determined by the forcing function x that is fed into the circuit. If one were to record the quantity y as a function of time and plot it against the function x, also as a function of time, the relationship y as a function of x could be obtained.

One of the very important characteristics of the analog computer in this form is that it is possible to investigate an equation such as the one solved in Fig. 3.4 for various values of coefficients of d^2y/dt^2, dy/dt, and y merely by changing the conductance and capacitance values in the circuit. The effect of various forms of the function $x(t)$ may also be evaluated. If the equation is one characterizing a control mechanism, it is possible to study the performance of this mechanism for a large number of different values of the parameters that might appear as coefficients of the various terms in the equation.

Figure 3.7 shows a mechanical system, consisting of a mass, a spring, and a damping device. The damper produces a resistance to motion proportional to the speed at which the mass m is moving, and directed opposite to the velocity. The motion of this system is

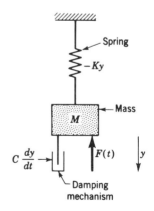

Fig. 3.7 Mass-spring-damper system.

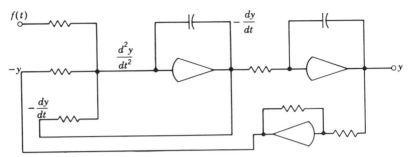

Fig. 3.8   Electrical analog of mass-spring-damper system.

represented by the following equation:

$$m \frac{d^2y}{dt^2} = -ky - C\frac{dy}{dt} + f(t) \qquad (3.21)$$

The force $f(t)$ is visualized as some external force acting on the system. This equation is in the same form as that represented by the circuit of Fig. 3.8. By manipulating the values of the resistances and the capacitances, the R's and C's of the circuit, it is possible to simulate the performance of the mass-spring-damping system on the analog computer. This yields the value of the displacement y as a function of time for any given values of mass, spring constant, and damping and an external forcing function $f(t)$. Much more complex systems than the simple mass-spring-damping system shown here can be analyzed by using these basic circuits in various combinations to represent the more complex systems, and relationships between the output and the input are obtained directly.

3.3.   The Digital Computer

The electronic digital computer with a high-speed electronic memory first became commercially available in the United States about 1950. This computer was the outgrowth of a long and continued effort to produce a computing machine that could perform calculations at an extremely high rate of speed and, in addition, would be able to carry out certain decision-making functions.

The electronic digital computer operates exclusively on numbers. The input to it and the output from it are in numerical form. It is necessary, therefore, to provide instructions for the machine in its own language, that of numbers, and enable it to translate its output into a usable form.

In a very general way, the capabilities of the electronic digital computer are fourfold. First, it is capable of providing numerical solutions of an arithmetic nature: for example, addition and subtraction, multiplication and division, and the various combinations of these. Secondly, it is capable of process control; machines can be controlled by digital computers to perform operations previously requiring guidance by human operators. The third capability is simulation; the computer can be programmed to simulate a real situation by means of a mathematical model of this reality. The fourth function is data processing: inventory control, for example.

We shall consider first its capabilities for solving equations by arithmetic means. The problem of finding the value of y in the equation

$$y = ab \tag{3.22}$$

can be solved very readily with a desk calculator. In order to carry out this operation, one records the value of a and the value of b. The value of a is introduced to the calculator and then the value of b, and the appropriate operation is performed to multiply one by the other. The value of y is recorded; then the machine is cleared and is ready for the next operation. If there is a list of values of a and b to be multiplied, one sets up a program of multiplying one by the other and recording the result of the operation in a suitable spot on a work sheet. A systematic procedure is the essence of this operation. It can be carried out by a reasonably intelligent clerk who is neat and orderly.

It would be pointless to carry on a single operation such as this by means of the electronic digital computer. However, if one had a list of quantities a and b numbering in the tens, hundreds, or more, it would be appropriate to program this on a computer and save a great deal of operator time. The computer could perform this operation very readily and would do so on the basis of a program that would cover essentially the following things:

1. READ the quantity a and the quantity b.
2. MULTIPLY quantity a by quantity b.

3. RECORD as quantity y the product of a and b obtained in previous operations.

4. PUNCH or PRINT the quantity y.

5. STOP the program.

If a large number of the quantities a and b were involved, one could then change the instructions, particularly the first step, and instruct the machine to read the values of a and b, respectively, and record them in its memory. The next instruction would be to take the appropriate values of a and b, multiply them, record the product as the quantity y, and either punch or print it out immediately or store it in the memory for future reference. However, after each calculation it would be necessary to instruct the machine to return to its list and select new values of a and b for the following operation of multiplication. Every detail of the operation must be incorporated in the program for the machine. One cannot rely on its good sense, as one can on a person making this calculation on a desk calculator.

The ability of the electronic digital computer to perform such operations as multiplication, division, addition, and subtraction is of basic importance. However, machines capable of these operations at high speeds, and nothing else, would not be as important as the electronic digital computer with memory. The modern digital computer can carry out basic arithmetic operations, make decisions on the basis of instructions that enable it to compare quantities, one with another or with some predetermined quantity, and record the results of its operations, either for immediate delivery to the output or for storage to be used in later operations or under conditions to be specified and determined by later operations.

The electronic digital computer is a powerful factor in modern business and engineering because of its ability to carry out numerical calculations, to make decisions, to record in its memory large quantities of data, and to find these stored items in extremely short periods of time. If it did not have access to the material stored in its memory in a period of time comparable with that required for the execution of a mathematical operation, the computer would have very limited value. For example, in the very simple problem suggested earlier, if the machine had a list of quantities a and b and it had to find these quantities before performing the multiplication operation, it would be pointless to be able to perform the actual multiplication in something of the order of a microsecond and then require a minute to locate the next value of a and b.   If the access time to the memory is roughly the same order of magnitude as the time required for the operations, a successful program can be carried out.

The capabilities of the electronic digital computer can be applied to the solution of algebraic equations, such as that illustrated above, when the number of calculations is so great that one can justify the use of the machine.   The solution of single algebraic equations cannot be justified.   Repetitious work, which is done poorly by many human beings, can be done extremely well by the computer.   Its versatility extends also to the solution of differential equations by the use of numerical methods.   This use is warranted if the differential equation is so complex that it cannot be solved by analytical methods or if the number of calculations to be made is so great that it cannot be carried out in a reasonable time by other methods.

To illustrate this in a very elementary manner, we consider solution of the equation $dy/dx = x^2$, with initial value $y = 5$ at $x = 0$.   This can be written as

$$\Delta y = x^2 \, \Delta x \tag{3.23}$$

A new value of y is equal to a previous one, incremented by an amount Δy; hence one writes

$$y_n = y_{n-1} + \Delta y \tag{3.24}$$

Similarly, for x,

$$x_n = x_{n-1} + \Delta x \tag{3.25}$$

Forming a table with columns headed x_n, x^2, Δx, Δy, and y, respectively, one can calculate the value of y as a function of x in a very elementary manner without even the use of a desk calculator if tractable values of x and y are used.   For example, let us assume increments of x equal to 0.1 and recall that the initial value of y is 5.   The tabulation is shown in Table 3.2.   When $x = 0.5$, y has attained the value of 5.030.   This compares fairly well with the value found by obtaining the analytical solution of the equation, which is

$$y = 5.0 + \frac{x^3}{3} \tag{3.26}$$

Table 3.2

x	$\dfrac{dy}{dx} = x^2$	Δx	Δy	y
0	0	0.1	0	5.000
0.1	0.01	0.1	0.001	5.000
0.2	0.04	0.1	0.004	5.001
0.3	0.09	0.1	0.009	5.005
0.4	0.16	0.1	0.016	5.014
0.5	0.25	0.1	0.025	5.030

Substituting the value $x = 0.5$ gives $y = 5.042$. The agreement can be improved significantly by decreasing the increment Δx. If $\Delta x = 0.05$ is used, the final value is 5.036.

It would be pointless to solve an equation as simple as this by means of the digital computer. However, differential equations of great complexity can be solved in the same manner; in fact, differential equations for which there is no known analytical solution can be solved by numerical methods. Since the time required for such numerical solutions on the digital computer is very short, it can be used advantageously.

A second application of the digital computer, namely, process control, is increasing in industrial applications, both where human control requires that the operator engage in very tedious functions and also in cases where a human operator is simply not adequate.

In chemical-process industries it is frequently impossible for a human operator to perform certain necessary functions as fast as is desired, but a computer can do the work. In the computer-controlled operation, the characteristics of the material in process are sensed throughout the plant, and these are compared with those prescribed for the process. The computer compares the measured values of the various quantities with those which are ideal and issues the commands necessary to correct any errors. The quantities that might be measured and transmitted to the computer are temperatures, pressures, rates of flow, and the like. If any of these quantities is greater or less than the desired value, the computer makes suitable calculations and comparisons to determine this fact and then issues corrective commands. This is accomplished by computing the difference in size of numerical quantities and comparing them, one with the other or with established values stored in its memory. In addition to making comparisons and issuing commands directed toward correcting any undesirable situations, the computer also controls the sequence of events in a process.

The computer is used extensively in the control of machine tools. It has been developed to the extent that the machine can read a drawing when presented to it in the proper form, generate the commands necessary to execute the process on the machine tool, monitor the progress of the operation, and make corrections during the operation to ensure satisfactory performance.

The third category of computer use is in simulation. This can be illustrated by a traffic-control problem. The traffic problem is represented by a mathematical statement describing the input to the area under consideration, the nature of the highways available, traffic controls that are in place or may be instituted, and the nature of the traffic flow in detail. The simulation process consists in feeding to the machine inputs describing the traffic coming to the area under the different conditions that must be studied. Various configurations of control devices can be incorporated in the model, and the output describes traffic under the conditions of input and control included on the model. In a very short time it is possible to simulate traffic conditions covering many days, weeks, or months of actual operation. The effect of human involvement can be considered by using mathematical techniques that describe the probable results of human decisions under particular traffic conditions.

The fourth area of application of the computer is in data processing, of which inventory control is a good example. An inventory of an industrial organization consists of a listing of materials stored and available for use. The inventory is increased by purchases and decreased by use, obsolescence, spoilage, and theft. The ideal situation would result when the exact quantity of every item on hand at a particular time could be known and controlled. The record keeping necessary in a large organization to approximate this ideal is so great that it cannot be handled in any realistic fashion without the use of high-speed computing equipment. Inputs to the computer are receipts, shipping reports, and the like. The outputs are indications of need for more material, a statement of shortage, bills, accounting records, and any derived material such as predictions of the rate at which material is being used or will be used and the time at which shortages might occur. It is necessary to store in the computer's memory names of customers, names of producers or suppliers, balances due, material on order and not received, material on order and not shipped, and any other detail that might be pertinent to a thorough understanding of the operation. This system would automatically provide bills to the customers and orders for new inventory material.

The reservation system used by both airlines and railroads is similar to an inventory system but has a somewhat different purpose. The objective of this system is to provide a means of handling rapidly requests for space reservations. This is a difficult problem, since reservations are made at a large number of points throughout the operating system. Centralized records must be kept of all space available, and as these spaces are reserved, the reservation must be recorded. A central computer can keep track of all flights or trains, all space on each, and all the reservations that have been made up to a particular time. The computer is connected to each reservation office, and at these points the operator places a request with the computer for space on a particular flight or train. The computer determines if such space is available; if it is, it so informs the clerk and the reservation can be confirmed or not, as the case may be. If no space is available, the clerk is so informed. If a cancellation is made, a similar process is carried through, the clerk informing the computer that a particular reservation has been canceled; this fact is recorded in the memory so that the space is available for future requests.

As the occasion demands, in our subsequent discussion of system design, we shall consider problems that lend themselves to solution by either digital- or analog-computer technique and, in addition, develop techniques necessary to carry out the solution of problems, either of analysis or synthesis, in system design.

Problems

In each of the following systems, consider whether a computer is required; if it is, describe its role in the system operation.

3.1. A centralized, technical library which stores all the important engineering and scientific information available in English, Japanese, Russian, French, and German in the year 1980, located in the city of Chicago.

3.2. The traffic-control system of the island of Manhattan in the year 1975.

3.3. The inventory-control system for a company with widely distributed branches, such as Sears Roebuck and Co.

3.4. An automatic, high-speed railroad train that has no crew on board responsible for the operation of the train.

3.5. An expressway system in which the automobiles would be controlled, not by their drivers, but by some system that would take over control of the car after it entered a certain lane on the expressway. This must provide for the control of speed and the exit from the express lane, as well as the entrance to it, from the entrances and exits of the expressway. All traffic on the expressway would be controlled by this system.

References

Doebelin, E. O.: "Dynamic Analysis and Feedback Control," pp. 58–75, McGraw-Hill Book Company, New York, 1962.

Goode, H. H., and R. E. Machol: "System Engineering," pp. 203–284, McGraw-Hill Book Company, New York, 1957.

Johnson, C. L.: "Analog Computer Techniques," 2d ed., McGraw-Hill Book Company, New York, 1963.

Lynch, W. A., and J. G. Truxal: "Signals and Systems in Electrical Engineering," pp. 355–421, McGraw-Hill Book Company, New York, 1962.

——— and ———: "Principles of Electronic Instrumentation," pp. 139–159, McGraw-Hill Book Company, New York, 1962.

Raven, Francis H.: "Automatic Control Engineering," pp. 129–149, McGraw-Hill Book Company, New York, 1961.

Sutherland, R. L.: "Engineering Systems Analysis," pp. 181–205, Addison-Wesley Publishing Company, Inc., Reading, Mass., 1958.

Evaluation and Test

4.1. Evaluation Criteria In Chap. 2 it was pointed out that a design is established, to a very considerable extent, by the selection of the criteria for optimization. In a comparable manner, the procedure for evaluating a system or one of its components is fixed by the criteria against which the evaluation is made.

Systems consist of components, which in turn must be evaluated. Ordinarily, the term testing, rather than evaluating, is used for subsystems or components. Component testing is a well-established branch of engineering for which professional engineering societies, governmental agencies, and other authoritative organizations have well-documented codes.

Test codes, with a long history supporting them, in many cases use the criterion of efficiency for both mechanical and electrical components. In the case of an electric motor, the ratio between the power output and the power input, the overall efficiency, is extremely important to a purchaser. It is easily defined and understood by everyone, and it can be measured directly and accurately. Procedures are standardized so that measurements yield comparable results in all tests.

The field of hydraulics employs the concept of efficiency as a valuable criterion. One is interested in the power required to drive a pump in order to obtain a given hydraulic output. In positive-displacement pumps, such as gear or piston pumps, two different efficiencies may be defined: one, the overall efficiency which is, as in the case of an electric motor, the ratio between the power output and the power input, and the other, a volumetric efficiency, which is the ratio of the rate of flow of the liquid to the ideal rate of flow that would be produced by an ideal or perfect pump. These two efficiencies describe performance over the entire operating range. Performance characteristics are defined more completely by both efficiencies than by one. A third efficiency, the mechanical efficiency, which is the overall efficiency divided by the volumetric efficiency, is defined as the ratio of ideal to actual torque input. Test procedures have not been established for positive-displacement pumps to the extent that they have for electric motors, steam boilers, and other electrical or mechanical devices; however, a comprehensive test code for centrifugal pumps exists.

In conclusion, therefore, the selection of criteria and the acceptance of these criteria by the public concerned with the testing procedure are vital and must precede the establishment of test procedures.

4.2. Evaluation of a System

In the complete evaluation of a system, the following elements, at least, must be included:

    1. Establishing criteria
    2. Creating a mathematical model
    3. Establishing component characteristics
    4. Testing components
    5. Testing subsystems
    6. Evaluating the system from the mathematical model

Once the objectives of the system design have been established and suitable criteria for optimization have been agreed upon, the description of the system in symbolic terms is undertaken. At this point, the use of a block diagram is frequently dictated by the complexity of the system. The very simple freeway system considered earlier does not require a block diagram, but its use is illustrated in Fig. 4.1. A single block describes the overall freeway system. The

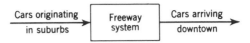

Fig. 4.1   Block diagram of freeway system.

input consists of cars originating in the suburbs, and at the other end the output is cars arriving downtown.   A more complete representation of the system would show origin of traffic throughout the system and discharge of this traffic at its destination in the various areas throughout the day.   However, for the present purposes, the simplified form suffices.   A more complex system requires a large number of boxes, various interconnections, and, if there is a traffic-control system, feedback of information on the traffic flow to the control is necessary.

The block diagram is very useful in visualizing a system and enabling the designer to establish reasonable interconnections and to be sure that the system is complete, but it is not adequate for a thorough analysis of the working of the system.   A more elaborate block diagram of the simple freeway system contributes to a more thorough understanding, as shown in Fig. 4.2.   Here the system is broken down into three components: the on ramps, the off ramps, and the express lanes.   Cars originate on the on ramps, proceed from them to the express lanes, and leave the system by means of the off ramps.   This facilitates discussion of the system in the preliminary planning stages but does not provide sufficient means for complete analysis of the traffic flow.

System performance or, as a matter of fact, any physical phenomenon is subject to description by mathematical means to overcome the difficulty suggested above.   If one describes the system represented by a block diagram in terms of mathematical equations, performance may be predicted by using well-established mathematical methods for the solution of the equations.   In the event that a straightforward analytical solution is not practical, numerical calculations, either with desk calculators or by hand or, if they are extremely complex, by means of high-speed computers, are in order.

A simple element of a system is pictured in Fig. 4.3.   Here is

Fig. 4.2   Block diagram of freeway system.

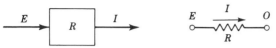

Fig. 4.3 Electrical element and block diagram.

shown a piece of wire with a resistance R, connected to two terminals, where the potential at one of them is E and at the other is zero. This is represented by a block diagram in Fig. 4.3, with the voltage E as the input, the element as the resistance R shown in the block, and the output the current I. This physical situation can be represented by a mathematical expression, as follows:

$$E = RI$$

If the total system consisted of electrical elements, for which similar equations can be written, the entire system could be analyzed by use of these equations and suitable mathematical tools. As implied earlier, the reduction of a system to a block diagram and then to a system of equations places in the hands of the designer all the power of the science of mathematics, with its methods for the solution of problems.

If the expressway system could be reduced to a system of equations in a similar manner, the solution of any problems that might arise would be greatly expedited. In the elementary feasibility study, the problem was expressed in relatively simple equations. However, these were gross simplifications of the real problem, and one might consider Fig. 4.2 in order to reveal some of the complexities found in such a problem. The flow onto the highway is Q_i, the input flow, and the flow off is Q_o, each expressed in terms of the number of cars per unit time. The length of expressway between an on ramp and an off ramp is L, and the number of cars per mile, that is, the density of the traffic, is N. One can write an equation describing the traffic flow as follows:

$$(Q_i - Q_o)\, dT = L\, dN$$

The term dT is an interval of time, and dN is the increment in density of cars during the time dT on the section of highway of length L.

If one were able to write this equation for each section of the highway between on ramp and off ramp, some insight could be obtained into the details of the traffic flow. If there were but a single section of highway of length L, with one on ramp and one off ramp, the solution of the problem would be straightforward. If the on flow Q_i exceeded the outflow, quite obviously the density of cars between the on and off ramps would increase and the rate at which it increased, dN/dT, would be obtained directly from this equation by rewriting it: $dN/dT = (Q_i - Q_o)/L$. If Q_i and Q_o were functions of time, as indeed they would be in a real situation, the rate at which the density of traffic between the on and off ramps changes would be a function of time, which might or might not be complex, depending upon the nature of the functions Q_i and Q_o. In any case, it would be possible to study a flow pattern of a freeway system if such equations were available.

Quite obviously, the determination of the functions Q_i and Q_o is the very essence of the problem, and if data are not available to describe these functions, not very much can be done to establish the characteristics of the system.

It is apparent that, if the evaluation of a system is to be possible, one must be able to describe the components of the system and their interrelations by means of mathematical equations. If one can do this with a system as a whole, he has created a mathematical model of the system.

The performance characteristics of each component of a system can be described by expressing the output of the component in terms of the input. The ratio of the output to the input is called the transfer function of the component. In the case of the simple resistor shown in Fig. 4.3, the ratio of the output I to the input E is $1/R$. The greater the resistance, the smaller the output for a given input. It is not always as easy as this to establish component characteristics, and much testing is devoted to this purpose.

Ideally, the system designer should be able to obtain transfer functions for all the components from the manufacturer. Unfortunately this ideal condition does not exist. Components must be tested to establish these transfer functions. The description of the system by block diagram and equation establishes the necessary transfer functions. For example, if the element of Fig. 4.3, a resistance, were a part of a system, and the desired current could be obtained with a resistance of 10 ohms, it is a very simple matter to purchase a 10-ohm resistor. However, if, instead of a simple resistor, the element were a hydraulic motor, the output of which is torque and the input to which is fluid flowing at a given rate and having a certain pressure, the relationships among the torque output, pressure, rate of flow, speed of rotation, etc., are not nearly as clear-cut as are the relationships among voltage, resistance, and current. If one were fortunate, the characteristics of the motor in terms of performance charts might be obtained from the manufacturer. Translating these into a useful mathematical equation presents considerable difficulty. If the charts were not available, tests would be indicated, and the results of this testing would be incorporated in the description of the system by means of a suitable equation or set of equations.

When components are assembled into subsystems, the performance of the subsystem must be checked against specifications. If the subsystem is not very large, simple testing will reveal the degree of agreement between the prediction of the equations and the actual performance. If the subsystem is relatively large itself, it may not be feasible to carry out simple tests to evaluate its performance. In this case, component tests, giving the transfer functions of the components, may be as far as one goes in actual physical testing. The transfer functions describing the characteristics of the components are then used in an evaluation of the subsystem by means of a mathematical model in order to predict performance.

This procedure is essential when one evaluates the system as a whole. It is seldom possible to carry out tests that would give a satisfactory indication of the performance of a system in terms of the criteria established for its evaluation.

In almost every case, the evaluation of a system is complicated by the fact that human beings are involved in one way or another. This would create no unusual problems if people could be considered in the same light as any other component of the system. The characteristics of the physical components of a system can be described in a quite straightforward manner. As indicated earlier, the transfer functions can be established for each of the elements of the system. The lifetime of a component will depend upon the quality of the materials and the workmanship incorporated in its manufacture. If the environment is in accordance with its design parameters, the component will perform without fatigue and at a high level for its full lifetime; in summary, its performance is predictable.

A human being does not perform in this straightforward manner. Environment is of great importance, and the environment includes not only the immediate vicinity of the system in which the person is participating but also the environment during the time preceding and even following his participation in the operation of the system. The interrelationships of various human beings in the system play an important part in their individual performances. The attitude of a person toward the task he is performing can be far more important than anything else that contributes to his action. The performance of human beings will be considered in more detail in a later section. For the time being, suffice it to say that the human element in a system is least subject to description by means of mathematical expressions and hence least predictable in every way.

4.3. Examples of System Evaluation

Difficulties encountered in evaluating systems will be illustrated by an example.[1] During the Second World War, an antiaircraft system was installed on merchant ships that were traveling in convoys. It was decided to evaluate the system by determining what percentage of sighted planes was actually brought down. This was the criterion for evaluation. The study revealed that a very small percentage of these planes was shot down; this observation engendered considerable discouragement.

However, further evaluation resulted in the conclusion that the criterion selected was not really the right one. The objective of the system was not to bring down planes but rather to protect ships in convoy. If all ships in the convoy made the trip successfully, it was of no importance how many aircraft were shot down. When it became apparent that the proper criterion for evaluation was the percentage of ships that got through in a given convoy, a completely different result was obtained. Simply having the guns on the ships kept the planes away, and the convoys with guns were in very much better condition than those without. The difference was a matter of several orders of magnitude, not a difference of a few percentage points. This is an excellent illustration of the vital importance of selecting the proper criterion for evaluation or optimization of a system.

The difficulty of evaluating a system when the system is very

[1] H. H. Goode and R. E. Machol, "System Engineering," pp. 123–124, McGraw-Hill Book Company, New York, 1957.

large and subject to a variety of inputs can be illustrated by considering the traffic-control system of a large city, wherein the inputs to the system vary from hour to hour during any given day. In the morning the commuters come to the city; during the day there is traffic within the city and a small amount coming in from the outside and a small amount going out; and at the end of the business day the commuters return to the suburbs, generating heavy traffic. At night, depending upon the local situation, there may or may not be a fairly heavy inflow early in the evening and a heavy outflow late in the evening. The daily traffic will vary somewhat during the week. Saturday and Sunday differ from regular working days. There may very well be a Friday afternoon exodus from the city and on Sunday afternoon and Monday morning a heavy inflow from the recreational areas around the city. Within the city, during any one day, the traffic flow is determined by many things. Local disturbances, such as storms, fires, and accidents, complicate the situation.

It would require a great deal of time to evaluate a traffic-control system, with freeways and all the necessary appurtenances, by observing what happened during an appropriately long period. Furthermore, one could not be certain that during the study period everything of importance would actually take place within the system. Indeed, there might be no serious accidents or fires. Perhaps there would be no long weekend contributing to the holiday traffic situation. It might be totally impractical to spend the amount of time necessary to establish the quality of the traffic-control system, assuming that an acceptable criterion for measuring quality could be agreed upon.

The necessity for a model of a traffic-control system is obvious. A mathematical model makes it possible to consider any conceivable input that might be compatible with the design. The performance of the system under these circumstances is revealed by a model study. One can have considerable confidence in the results of such a study provided that the elements of the system are thoroughly understood and properly represented by transfer functions in the mathematical model. A study of this sort could include disturbances that might not arise for a very long time in the real case, as well as factors that would be dangerous in the real-life situation. It would then be possible to anticipate difficulties that needed rectifying and to provide for improved performance.

It is necessary to develop confidence in the use of a mathematical model in system evaluation. There is a tendency to feel that actual test is better than the modeling of a system. The impracticability of test on a very large scale and the need for compression of the time scale if one must observe the effect of all possible inputs on the system dictate use of a model to establish the merit of the method by observing the correlation between the predicted performance and the real performance at later times. There is indeed a real difference between the evaluation of a system in this manner and the simple test of a component. If the transfer functions of all the elements of a system are known with a reasonable degree of accuracy, the overall performance can be predicted with confidence. In certain cases, the performance of a component is critical, and if it varies even a small amount from that indicated by its transfer function, instability in the system might arise. However, such instabilities or critical points can be predicted ahead of time and extreme care taken in the evaluation of the particular components involved. If it be a portion of the circuitry that is critical, a similar investigation will reveal its adequacy.

The model has an additional advantage in the evaluation of performance in that one can introduce unexpected, infrequent, or hazardous inputs and determine what the system performance will be under these circumstances. For example, a freeway system could not be tested in terms of certain unusual inputs in the field, but it would be perfectly feasible to do this in a model. One could introduce extremely high traffic densities in certain areas, whereas such traffic densities might not be observed in the real case in the near future. One could also remove from operation any part of the system and determine its effect on the whole. In general, then, the model gives much greater flexibility in evaluation than does the system itself.

4.4. Human Factors

Problems arising from the presence of people in a system are different in kind from those associated with other components. If human reaction to any situation could be predicted, a transfer function for the human beings in the system would be available for all circumstances. Such is certainly not now the case, nor is it likely ever to be.   Human beings have individuality, and only under extremes of controlled conditions can human reactions be predicted.   A controlled experiment involving a person is possible, but difficult to arrange, and is feasible only for limited activities.   Human performance is unequaled in the solution of complex problems, but this ability is not subject to exact measurement in the same sense that the performance of an electric motor can be measured.   Among the abilities possessed by people and not by a machine is their ability to recognize qualitative as contrasted with quantitative information.

Although a computing machine must be addressed in the language peculiar to its operation, and with absolute accuracy in grammar, punctuation, and the like, one human being can convey information to another in very sloppy language, either spoken or written. In fact, people can communicate in very degraded forms of a language when one of them is not well versed in the language of the other.   Errors in grammar, punctuation, and spelling may reduce clarity but do not eliminate the possibility of accurately conveying information.

A person can handle redundant information and select from that stored in memory useful parts when and if needed.   A distinguishing characteristic of the human being is the ability to recognize form and shape even though the symbol may not be exact.   For example, a person has no particular difficulty in reading many different type forms.   The language may be expressed in handwriting, typed copy, printed copy, or other form, all equally intelligible.   It has been only recently that machines have had any of this ability at all.   Some now being designed are capable of reading the printed word.   However, there still remains a difference in that a machine designed to read, for example, German script would not be able to read English script. It would recognize almost nothing in the English script that could elicit a response.   On the other hand, the human being educated to read English, while unable to read the German language, can still recognize forms in the characters of the language and distinguish and describe them to another person.

In terms of basic capabilities such as memory, human beings have both advantages and disadvantages.   The human memory capacity is much greater than that of any contemporary machine. However, the access time, that is, the time required to recall a particular piece of information, is usually very much shorter in the machine than in man.   People recall frequently used items almost immediately, but it sometimes requires a very extensive search of the memory to elicit a piece of information stored there a long time back and unused in the interim.

Human beings suffer weaknesses that are of great importance in system operation. Among these are overloading, fatigue, inability to perform as precisely as required, and inability to respond in a manner compatible with the situation.

Overloading occurs when the demands on a person are greater than can be borne, either physically, mentally, or emotionally. In emergency situations, pilots of aircraft may find it totally impossible to respond to all the demands placed upon them, and after the accident occurs the judgment is "pilot failure." Overloading may occur in many systems, but we are sometimes unaware of it unless disaster results, as in aircraft accidents.

Mental and physical fatigue is familiar to people. Machines, in general, do not have this weakness except under extreme circumstances. After a person has become fatigued, his response is inferior to that when he is fresh. In system operation, requiring high performance by human beings, long periods of activity cannot be countenanced if resulting fatigue causes deterioration of performance.

The demands on the human sensory capacity in terms of precision are coming to be well understood. If, in the design of a system, this has been overlooked, substandard performance may well be the result. For example, a person may not be able to read a gauge with the accuracy required, or it may be impossible for him to distinguish between two quantities with the precision necessary for good operation.

Natural habits, or response patterns, may not be compatible with those required in the operation of a system. It is difficult for a person to make motions independently with his two hands in certain directions and sequences. This must be considered when designing an operation by a human being in a system.

In summary, people are used in systems and will continue to be for a long time because they have certain abilities that have not been equaled by the machine, and they have certain adaptive characteristics now being considered for machines but not successfully developed as yet. A particular capability of the human being is flexibility; this is not a distinguishing feature of the machine. In an emergency, a human being can adapt behavior to the situation. He is able to exercise judgment and reasoning power beyond the capability of the machine except in certain prescribed situations where the routine has been built in.   The machine, on the other hand, excels, for example, in repetitive and routine tasks, which it can do time after time without becoming bored or inattentive.   The ability of the machine to carry out computations of a repetitive and routine nature is totally beyond the capability of a human being.   Human ability to carry on a great number of simultaneous activities is also very limited, in contrast to that of machines, which have no such limitation.

Problems

In each of the following problems, select a criterion for the evaluation of the system.

4.1.   An automatic, high-speed railroad, serving a commuter clientele from the suburbs to the center of a large city.

4.2.   A freeway system for a large city, which supplies service for both commuters and through highway traffic passing through the center of the city.

4.3.   The reservation system of an airline operating throughout the United States.

4.4.   The traffic-control system of the downtown section of a large city.

4.5.   An information storage and retrieval system—in other words, a library—for a city with a population of 1 million.

References

Asimow, Morris: "Introduction to Design," pp. 7–11, 84–85, Prentice-Hall, Inc., Englewood Cliffs, N.J., 1962.

Ellis, D. O., and F. J. Ludwig: "Systems Philosophy," pp. 44, 64–68, Prentice-Hall, Inc., Englewood Cliffs, N.J., 1962.

Goode, H. H., and R. E. Machol: "System Engineering," pp. 123–129, 481–500, 508–512, McGraw-Hill Book Company, New York, 1957.

Gosling, W.: "The Design of Engineering Systems," pp. 188–189, 207–227, John Wiley & Sons, Inc., New York, 1962.

Hall, Arthur D.: "A Methodology for Systems Engineering," pp. 104–105, 165–166, 324–335, D. Van Nostrand Company, Inc., Princeton, N.J., 1962.

Mathematical Models and Methods 5

5.1. Need for a Model The desirability of predicting probable performance before a system is designed in detail has already been emphasized. Prediction of performance is based upon the relationships between inputs and outputs of the various system components and those of the system as a whole. The concept of the transfer function, the relationship between the output and the input, and the use of a mathematical model to provide a description of system performance were discussed in Sec. 4.2. This relatively new concept has become an indispensable feature of system engineering.

Before the advent of formal system design, it was the practice to build a physical model, either small scale or full scale, depending to a considerable extent on the cost involved. The model was tested and, if satisfactory, put into production. Much more likely, its performance would fall short of expectations, and corrections were made, resulting ultimately in a prototype acceptable for use in final design and production. This was a costly process, but nothing better was available at the time. In the case of a successful manufactured product, the costs of development, making the model, and the testing thereof were minor compared with the profits ultimately derived. As components became more complex, high performance was expected, the costs of producing and testing models increased, and pressures arose for better prediction of performance to reduce development costs. The mathematical model came into being in response to these pressures, although it was not recognized as such in the terms used today.

The early use of the mathematical model involved crude designs on paper and an attempt to predict performance by means of the best theoretical concepts available. Not infrequently this required gross simplifications in order to secure tractable mathematical representations of the expected performance. The predictions could be no more reliable than the assumptions and simplifications on which they were based and were therefore frequently inadequate.

The failure of such models to predict performance accurately fostered the development of two schools of thought, one the practical and the other the theoretical. The practical person had little patience with a highly theoretical model of a machine or process and the prediction of performance from this model. He was much more impressed by the failures than by the successes of the method. He insisted that it was necessary to have a physical prototype available for test.

However, as complexity and cost increased, the use of a mathematical model to predict performance before actual construction began came to be recognized as the only practical method of design. Concurrently, development of the high-speed computer made possible analysis of performance by the mathematical model with fewer simplifying assumptions and therefore greater probability of success.

In summary, the mathematical model is a necessary tool of the engineer who designs complex machines and systems. It effects economies, it makes possible optimization of design, and, as the computers and theoretical background improve, predicted performance can be expected to be in better agreement with the actual performance of the physical prototype.

5.2. Purpose of the Mathematical Model

A mathematical model of a system or a component is used for the analysis of all pertinent features of the model and for prediction of the performance of the prototype. It makes the knowledge and techniques of the science of mathematics powerful, readily available tools for such analysis and prediction.

A mathematical model can be established if the proposed component or system has been described in words or in the form of sketches or drawings. The graphical or word descriptions are translated into equations in terms of a set of variables called the parameters of the system; they represent the various inputs, outputs, and internal connections. For example, some of the parameters of an electrical system are the resistances, capacitances, and inductances of the various elements. The effect of each parameter on system or component performance can be studied by adjusting the values in the mathematical model and observing the changes in predicted performance as a function of the variation in the parameters.

The nature of the equations depends upon the characteristics of the system. In some cases, a simple algebraic equation will suffice; in others, very complex differential equations may be needed. Once the equations have been written, the characteristics of the system may be explored. If solutions of the equations are obtainable, the output of the system may be expressed explicitly in terms of the input.

There are two distinct phases in the use of the mathematical model. Beginning with a graphical description of the physical system, the engineer establishes a model that represents the system in a useful manner. This model, in the form of equations, is then employed to describe the performance of the system by finding solutions of the equations.

It is appropriate, at this time, to consider the significance of the two, quite distinct operations: writing the equations and obtaining solutions. At first it may appear that setting up the equation is a relatively simple procedure and that obtaining a solution presents the real challenge. It is quite true that solving difficult mathematical equations is an interesting, profitable, and important task. However, the ultimate solution can be no better than the original equations, and if these fail to represent physical systems properly, the final mathematical solution will be worthless. Preoccupation with the details and elegance of solutions frequently obscures the extreme importance of the writing of the original equations describing the physical system. It is impossible to overemphasize the need for skill in writing the equations. It can be developed by practice; the important elements of success are the ability to separate the relevant from the irrelevant, discern orders of magnitude, and select suitable means of descriptions in terms of mathematical equations.

The use of the mathematical model is a multistep process, which may be repeated several times in the course of a design. From the graphical description of the physical system, mathematical equations are written to describe performance of the components. These equations are solved, and the solutions are compared with the known performance of the components. If the prediction is inadequate, a revision of the equations is undertaken. New solutions are sought, and comparison is again made. After satisfactory agreement has been obtained, the transfer functions are interrelated by means of equations describing the circuitry of the system. The performance of the system is then predicted by means of the model. The effect of varying the parameters is studied, and optimization of performance is undertaken. When the agreement between predicted system performance and specifications is satisfactory, design proceeds.

The process of devising a mathematical model, seeking a solution of the equations, and comparing the solutions with expected or actual performance will now be illustrated.

5.3. Examples of Mathematical Models

To illustrate the making of a mathematical model, solving the equations, and comparing the solutions with the operations of the physical system, three elementary cases will be discussed.

Figure 5.1 shows a system consisting of a mass, a spring, and a

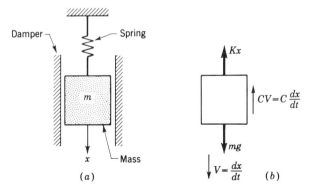

Fig. 5.1 Mass-spring-damper system.

Fig. 5.2 Block diagram
of force-mass system.

viscous damping mechanism that produces a frictional force opposing
the motion of the mass. The mass is suspended by the spring and
moves between two surfaces which are lubricated. If the mass is
pulled downward by an external force and then released, the spring
tends to pull it upward, and the viscous drag on its sides resists this
upward motion. In addition, the gravitational force pulls the mass
downward. These three external forces acting on the mass are
shown in Fig. 5.1*b*. The spring force acts upward and is proportional to the downward displacement x from the rest position and the
spring constant K. Viscous force acting on the sides is proportional
to the speed V and oppositely directed; hence it acts upward when
the motion is downward. The gravitational force is downward and
has a magnitude mg.

In order to describe the behavior of the mass-spring-damper
system, the mathematical model must give proper consideration to
the various forces acting on the mass and describe the consequent
motion of the mass itself.

This system is represented in two ways in Figs. 5.1 and 5.2.
The sketch in Fig. 5.1 is the conventional one for the representation
of this system, the free-body diagram. In Fig. 5.2 the system is
represented by a block diagram; the box represents the system with
the input a force F, and the output a displacement x. We are interested, in this case, in determining the output, displacement x, in
terms of the force system, which is the input to the box. Regardless of the method used to depict the system graphically, it is necessary to devise a mathematical model of the system that will describe
its motion. There is in physical theory an equation representing the
motion of such a system. It is known as Newton's second law of
motion and can be written either as an algebraic or a differential
equation as follows:

$$F = ma \tag{5.1a}$$

$$\text{or} \quad F = m\frac{d^2x}{dt^2} \tag{5.1b}$$

These equations describe the motion of a small particle of mass m, acted upon by an external force F, in terms of the time t and distance x. The force F, in the case of the system in Fig. 5.1, is the sum of the three external forces. The second derivative of x with respect to t, d^2x/dt^2, is the acceleration a. The sum of the three forces must be equal to the right-hand sides of Eqs. (5.1). Finally, then, the equation describing this particular system is

$$mg - CV - Kx = ma \qquad (5.2a)$$

$$\text{or} \quad mg - C\frac{dx}{dt} - Kx = m\frac{d^2x}{dt^2} \qquad (5.2b)$$

Here V is the velocity equal to dx/dt, and K is the spring constant. In either of these forms the equation is not particularly useful to describe the displacement x as a function of time. It is necessary, therefore, to seek a solution that will describe the position of the mass as a function of time. The solution of the differential equation can be obtained, but the details of this process are not appropriate here. We state the solution as follows:

$$x = C_1 e^{(-n+\sqrt{n^2-p^2})t} + C_2 e^{(-n-\sqrt{n^2-p^2})t} + \frac{mg}{K} \qquad (5.3)$$

where $n = C/2m$ and $p = \sqrt{K/m}$. The value of the constants C_1 and C_2 in Eq. (5.3) is determined by the initial conditions in the system at the time $t = 0$. The position of the mass and either its velocity or acceleration at the time $t = 0$ must be known in order to evaluate these constants. If the mass starts from rest at the position $x = 0$, both C_1 and C_2 are fixed in value.

The form of Eq. (5.3) is such that the nature of the relationship between x and t depends on the values of n and p. If the quantity n^2 is large compared with p^2, and the exponents are therefore negative real quantities, the solution is an exponential relationship between x and t, and x decreases continuously as t increases. Physically, this means that the damping force is relatively large compared with the spring force, and if the mass is displaced from the position of equilibrium and released, it will gradually approach the equilibrium position, will never reach it, and certainly will not go beyond it. If the quantity n^2 is small compared with p^2, that is, there is a relatively small damping force, then the term $n^2 - p^2$ is negative, the exponent is a complex quantity, and the solution is in the form of a series of trigonometric terms, sines and cosines. This indicates an oscillatory motion, that is, x is a periodic function of t. Under these circumstances, if the mass is displaced from the equilibrium position and released, it will move back to and then beyond the equilibrium position and set up an oscillatory motion that continues with time until the energy has been dissipated by the damping force.

If this system consisted of the mass and spring only, the motion would be oscillatory, as would be intuitively expected. Displacing the mass from its equilibrium position and releasing it result in an up-and-down motion that continues so long as there is no external damping force to dissipate the energy. The solutions of Eqs. (5.2), given in Eqs. (5.3) and discussed above, do indeed accurately describe the motion of such a system. This system is a classical one and has been investigated thoroughly. It has been found that such systems can be represented satisfactorily by these equations.

One should note that Eq. (5.1a and b), which is Newton's second law of motion, is adequate only for terrestrial problems where the velocities are small and the mass is a reasonable size, but if the mass is a small particle, such as those encountered in modern physics research, Eq. (5.1a) no longer constitutes a suitable model. Relativistic effects must be taken into consideration when the velocity approaches that of light. It is necessary, therefore, to know ahead of time the general nature of the system to determine whether it can be represented by Newton's second law of motion or whether relativistic and other effects must be considered. The use of Newton's second law of motion was discovered to be inadequate in astrophysics during the nineteenth century. This discovery was a motivating force toward the formulation of Einstein's theory of relativity and many recent developments in modern physics.

To compare the predictions of the model for Fig. 5.1 with the actual performance, it would be necessary to measure the displacement x as a function of time, to measure the spring constant K, to measure the damping coefficient C, and to determine the mass of the block suspended by the spring. The amplitude of the oscillation and its frequency are subject to direct measurement. These could be compared with the predictions of the theory and the adequacy of the result could then be judged.

Figure 5.3 represents graphically a system very different from

Fig. 5.3   Block diagram of servicing center.

that shown in Fig. 5.1.   The block represents a service counter, as
might exist in a supermarket, gasoline station, or other customer-
service organization.   The input to the system is customers seeking
service.   The output is customers who have been served or who
decide to leave before being served or upon finding no service available.   Writing equations to describe this system presents problems
different from those of the previous example.

Before proceeding to the details of a mathematical model, we
consider, in Fig. 5.4, an analogous situation.   Here we have a tank
into which liquid is being supplied from a pipe at the rate of Q_i units
of volume per unit time and is being withdrawn from the tank at the
rate of Q_o units of volume per unit time.   The input is Q_i; the
output can be considered to be either Q_o or H, depending upon the
viewpoint.   If we consider H as the output, then Q_o is a negative
input.   Using this approach, we write the equation

$$(Q_i - Q_o)\, dt = A\, dH \tag{5.4}$$

This states simply that the sum of the inputs, $Q_i - Q_o$, multiplied by
an interval of time dT, represents the amount of liquid introduced
into the tank during this time.   The quantity of liquid must be equal

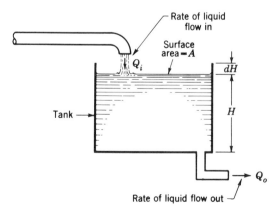

Fig. 5.4   Tank-filling operation.

to the change in volume in the tank itself during this period, since no liquid is created or destroyed, and is represented by the surface area A times the incremental depth dH.

The system of Fig. 5.3, which provides services to customers appearing at a central area to request this service, can be described by an equation of a form similar to Eq. (5.4); thus,

$$(Q_i - Q_o)\, dt = A\, dN \tag{5.5}$$

In these cases, the quantities Q_i and Q_o have similar meanings. In Fig. 5.3, Q_i is the rate at which customers arrive at the service area and Q_o is the rate at which they leave the area. In Fig. 5.4, Q_i is the rate at which liquid is supplied and Q_o the rate at which it is removed. The quantity dt is an interval of time; the area A in Fig. 5.3 represents a length of line or a service area, and dN the number of customers per unit area or length, for example, the number of customers per waiting line. In Fig. 5.4, A is the surface area of the liquid and dH the change in depth of liquid in time dt.

In the cases of the customer-service area and the liquid-storage tank, the mathematical description of the inputs and outputs, Q_i and Q_o, is basic to the problem. If Q_i and Q_o are analytical functions of time or are constant, solution of either problem is direct. If, on the other hand, Q_i is a random function of time, solution requires techniques different from those used in the solution of the equation describing the system in Fig. 5.1. Regardless of the nature of the inputs, Eqs. (5.4) and (5.5) are models of the systems shown in Figs. 5.3 and 5.4.

It is pertinent to discuss here the nature of the equations that describe the three systems shown in Figs. 5.1, 5.3, and 5.4. In the case of Fig. 5-1, the model is an equation describing the dynamics of a physical system in terms of the relationship among acceleration, force, and mass. The systems in Figs. 5.3 and 5.4 are described by equations that can properly be called conservation equations. This is easily visualized for the system of Fig. 5.4, the equation for which states simply that the rate at which mass increases inside the tank is equal to the difference in the rate at which it comes in and the rate at which it leaves the tank. If more comes into the tank than goes out of the tank, it must be stored in the tank; no mass is created or destroyed in the process. The same reasoning applies to the situation

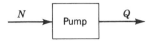

Fig. 5.5 Block diagram
of pump.

in Fig. 5.3; all the customers who enter the service area must be accounted for: Either they leave, or they stay in place in a waiting line.

Although description of the operation of a system component or a system as a whole raises problems of selection of the proper mathematical model, the three cases described thus far are quite straightforward and do not require extensive consideration to determine a reasonable mathematical model. The next illustration will point out some of the difficulties encountered in establishing a suitable mathematical model.

Figure 5.5 represents, in the form of a block diagram, a positive-displacement pump which pumps a relatively fixed quantity of liquid at each revolution of the shaft. One might consider the input to this pump to be the speed at which the shaft is rotated, N, in revolutions per unit time; the output, the rate at which liquid is delivered, Q, in units of volume per unit time. The pump itself has a physical characteristic known as the displacement D, the number of units of volume displaced ideally per revolution of the shaft. If this were an ideal pump, a mathematical model of its performance would be

$$Q = DN \tag{5.6}$$

This states simply that the rate at which liquid is delivered by the pump, Q units of volume per unit time, is equal to the product of the displacement per revolution, D, and the rate of rotation of the shaft, N. Each time the shaft rotates once, the quantity D is delivered. For some purposes, this would be an adequate model.

If one were to subject a pump to a test, he would find that under useful operating conditions the rate of delivery, Q, would be less than DN. A much better mathematical model of such a pump is the following equation:

$$Q = DN - C_s \frac{\Delta p D}{2 \pi \mu} \tag{5.7}$$

In this equation, C_s is a coefficient of slip and is dimensionless. The pressure differential between the discharge side of the pump and the inlet side of the pump is Δp. The viscosity of the liquid being pumped is μ. This equation incorporates a method of describing the physical fact that, when a pressure differential exists between the high-pressure and low-pressure sides of the pump, there is a flow— the slip—from the high to the low pressure through small passages inside the pump which exist to provide clearances between moving parts. This mathematical model of the pump gives a much better description of its performance than Eq. (5.6).

However, even this expression is not perfect since there are conditions under which the delivery Q will be even less than that indicated by Eq. (5.7). This can occur when the inlet conditions are not ideal and the pressure at the inlet side of the pump is so low that the pumping cavities do not fill completely with liquid but partially with vapor. This condition should not exist in good in-

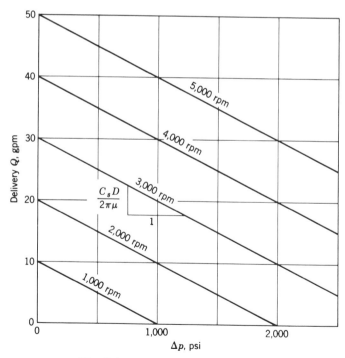

Fig. 5.6 Delivery of positive-displacement pump.

stallations; hence one can justify Eq. (5.7) if the system is well designed.

Equation (5.6) was the model used for a positive-displacement pump for some years, but when pumps of this type were employed in hydraulic systems it was learned that this model was inadequate and a more accurate description of performance was sought. The adequacy of any model, such as Eq. (5.7), can be tested only by experimental means. Figure 5.6 shows experimental data describing the performance of a positive-displacement pump. Here the general form of the experimentally determined performance is in accordance with Eq. (5.7). As the pressure increases, the delivery, at any given speed, decreases linearly. When there is no pressure differential Δp, the delivery Q increases with speed. From a plotting such as Fig. 5.6 the coefficient C_s can be determined, provided the value of the viscosity μ is known. The slope of the lines is $C_s D/2\pi\mu$. If viscosity μ is known, then the coefficient C_s can be calculated. Since the lines appear to be parallel, the coefficient C_s is a constant in this particular case, at least.

5.4. The Transfer Function

The relationship between the output of a component or system and its input has been defined as a transfer function. If this relationship is described by a differential equation, the transfer function is an operational transfer function that represents the general dynamic relationship in terms of the system parameters and a differential operator.[1]

If the relationship can be expressed by an algebraic equation, the transfer function is an algebraic operator. As an example of the latter, consider a positive-displacement pump represented by

$$Q = D_p N \tag{5.6}$$

The output is Q and the input is N. The transfer function is the ratio of the two; thus,

$$\frac{Q}{N} = D_p \tag{5.8}$$

[1] E. O. Doebelin, "Dynamic Analysis and Feedback Control," p. 83, McGraw-Hill Book Company, New York, 1962.

A differential operator is necessary to describe the system consisting of flows into and out of a tank of liquid. The equation for this system is

$$(Q_i - Q_o)\, dt = A\, dH \qquad\qquad (5.9)$$

The input is $Q_i - Q_o$, the sum of positive and negative flows, and the output is the depth of liquid, H. The transfer function is the ratio of H to $Q_i - Q_o$, thus

$$\frac{H}{Q_i - Q_o} = \frac{1}{A\,(d/dt)}$$

If the operator d/dt is replaced by D_t, we have

$$\frac{H}{Q_i - Q_o} = \frac{1}{A\,D_t} \qquad\qquad (5.10)$$

The physical meaning of the transfer function of the pump, D_p, is straightforward conceptually. Each time the pump shaft rotates through one revolution, a quantity of liquid, D_p, is carried from the intake to the discharge port and delivered to the pipe which carries it away.

In the second case, the physical meaning of the transfer function is more difficult conceptually. The operator D_t must not be confused with the quantity D_p used above for pump displacement. The operator D_t denotes differentiation with respect to time. When D_t operates on a quantity such as H, the result is the rate of change of H with respect to time. The operator $1/D_t$ denotes the inverse of differentiation, namely, integration. This transfer function indicates an integration or summation process which yields a quantity of liquid in the tank. This volume divided by the area A is the increment in the depth H. The increment will be positive when Q_i is greater than Q_o and negative when Q_o exceeds Q_i.

If the liquid is supplied to the tank by a pump with a transfer function given by

$$\frac{Q_i}{N} = D_p \qquad\qquad (5.8)$$

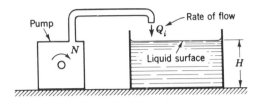

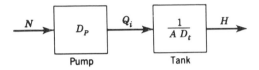

Fig. 5.7 Schematic and block diagrams of pump and reservoir.

and there is no outflow, the total system is shown in Fig. 5.7. The transfer function of the system is, then,

$$\frac{H}{N} = D_p \frac{1}{AD_t} \tag{5.11}$$

This can be rewritten as

$$D_p N = AD_t H$$

or $\quad Q_i = A \dfrac{dH}{dt} \tag{5.12}$

which is Eq. (5.9) when $Q_o = 0$.

   With components connected in series, as are the pump and tank, the transfer functions are also in series, or, as frequently stated, in tandem, and the overall transfer function is the product of the individual transfer functions. Analysis of system performance by use of transfer functions in complex systems is greatly facilitated since the algebra of transfer-function analysis is well established.

5.5. Using a Mathematical Model

The process of establishing a mathematical model for a component of a system can be described in the following terms:

1. A mathematical model is set up as a first approximation on the basis of theoretical considerations and any qualifying factors known from experience to influence the performance.

2. The equations forming the model are solved, and the resulting predictions of performance are placed in usable form.

3. The prediction of the solutions is compared with experience, in the form of experimental results if possible.

4. If the deviations from the predictions are too great, the model is corrected.

5. A new solution is obtained, and this solution is compared with experimental data.

6. The process is repeated as often as is necessary to obtain satisfactory agreement between prediction and actual performance.

A similar procedure is used for the system as a whole but with modifications dictated by the facts of the case.

The model of a system cannot be checked completely in accordance with steps 3 to 6 since its performance will not be known until construction is complete. The great value of a system model lies in the fact that, if the models of the components have been checked thoroughly by this procedure, the predictions of the system model will be reliable.

The model is used to predict system performance as follows:

1. A mathematical model is established using components, transfer functions, and the block diagram of the system to determine relationships between components.

2. The equations of the model are solved and the predictions made as graphs, tables, or such other form as may be appropriate.

3. The predictions are compared with specified performance.

4. If predicted performance is not in accord with specifications, parameters are changed and new predictions made.

5. The process of prediction, changing parameters, and prediction is repeated until acceptable results are obtained.

In the review of the predictions of system performance, the experienced engineer must apply his judgment, since he soon learns

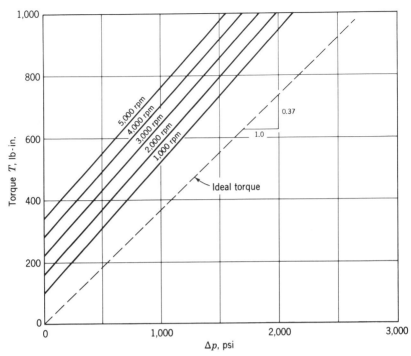

Fig. 5.8 Input torque of positive-displacement pump.

that even the best model does not always predict realistically. He must be alert to the possibility of order-of-magnitude errors and gross violations of common sense.

The procedure for a component will be illustrated now by considering the case of the positive-displacement pump discussed in Secs. 5.3 and 5.4. The mathematical model described the output of the pump in terms of fluid flow, but it was stated that the pump developed a pressure at the discharge side. This can also properly be considered an output of the pump. In this connection, a proper input would be the torque input. If the pump is to be driven by a motor, it is necessary to know the torque requirements to rotate the shaft under various operating conditions. Theoretical considerations indicate that the torque required to drive an ideal positive-displacement pump, i.e., one with no internal friction or other losses, can properly be represented by the expression

$$T_i = \frac{\Delta p D}{2\pi} \qquad (5.13)$$

Here, T_i is the ideal input torque to drive a pump of displacement D units of volume per revolution against a pressure differential Δp units of force per unit area.

The evaluation of this equation as a suitable mathematical model requires testing the pump at different pressures and speeds with liquids of various viscosities. Then a comparison of the output of the pump and the torque input would reveal the adequacy of Eq. (5.13). Experimental data of this nature are shown in Fig. 5.8. The experimental data (solid lines) are for a single pump with various speeds of operation and the same liquid throughout. The dashed line indicates Eq. (5.13). It is clear that this equation is not an adequate description of the relationship between the output Δp and the input T_i. When Δp is zero, the input torque depends upon the speed. It is also clear that the slope of the lines for constant-speed operation is not parallel to the dashed line representing Eq. (5.13). This indicates that the rate of increase of the torque requirement is not properly represented by the quantity $D/2\pi$, as Eq. (5.13) would require. However, the lines are parallel; hence a multiplying factor applied to $D/2\pi$ would correct this deficiency.

In order to investigate the relationship between the torque requirement and speed, the intercepts, at $\Delta p = 0$ of Fig. 5.8, are plotted in Fig. 5.9 as a function of the speed N. The intercept at $\Delta p = 0$ is called T_o. We note that T_o increases linearly with N but that, when N is zero, T_o is not zero. This residual torque is inde-

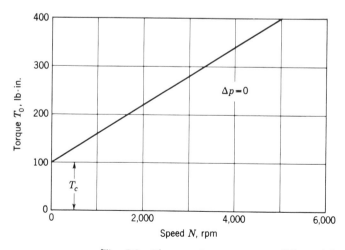

Fig. 5.9 Torque at zero pressure differential.

pendent of both speed and pressure. Its existence would not surprise a person familiar with this type of pump. He knows that, even though the pressure is zero and the shaft is not in rotation, a significant amount of torque is required to start it rotating.

Consideration of these physical facts leads one to the conclusion that frictional effects in this pump are large and important. Frictional effects, which depend on speed, are likely to be caused by viscous friction originating at surfaces that are moving relative to one another and are separated very small distances by a viscous liquid in the pump. An increase of torque at a rate greater than $D/2\pi$, as in Fig. 5.9, indicates a frictional force that depends upon pressure. This could arise from deformation of parts under pressure, causing an increase in a nonviscous frictional force. The friction remaining after speed and pressure have both been eliminated, as in Fig. 5.9, is a dry or coulomb friction originating at unlubricated surfaces that are forced together by a pressure inherent in the pump, probably caused by close fits. Seals cause frictional torques independent of speed and pressure. These experimentally determined facts can be incorporated in a mathematical model to describe better the performance of such a pump, as follows:

$$T = \frac{\Delta p D}{2\pi}(1 + C_f) + C_d \mu N D + T_c \qquad (5.14)$$

Here the coefficient C_f is a dimensionless factor describing the dry friction, which is pressure-dependent, independent of speed, and is shown in Fig. 5.8 as the cause of the difference between the slope of the dashed line and the solid line. Coefficient C_d is a coefficient of viscous friction and, together with the viscosity of the liquid, μ, accounts for the slope of the line in Fig. 5.9. The torque T_c is a constant, derived from friction at surfaces that are unlubricated and tightly fitting. This model is found, in practice, to be a reasonably good representation of the relationships among pressure, torque, speed, and viscosity of a positive-displacement pump.

Although progress has been made in developing a mathematical model, as is illustrated in Eq. (5.14), the situation is not perfect; much remains to be done to develop a better model for the positive-displacement pump, particularly with internal heating affecting viscosity.

It is pertinent at this point to note that components, such as hydraulic pumps and motors and mechanical devices, including internal-combustion engines, turbines, etc., are much more difficult to represent by satisfactory mathematical models than are electrical components. Mechanical phenomena cannot always be described by linear equations. Clearances vary, and physical properties of fluids are functions of pressure and temperature; all these complicate the relationships inherent in a mechanical energy-conversion system.

5.6. System Characteristics

An analysis of system behavior will reveal important characteristics that must be considered in producing a satisfactory design. A system is described in terms of a set of variables, commonly called design parameters, by means of which the system performance is described in the solution of the equations of the model. In the freeway system discussed earlier, the number of lanes of traffic is a design parameter. The number of on ramps, the number of off ramps, and the number of lanes in an off ramp are design parameters. The speed limits at various parts of the freeway likewise are parameters.

After one decides upon the value of a particular parameter, he is interested to know what effect it has on the overall system design or, in the case of a particular component, its effect on the performance of that particular component. For example, it would be appropriate to consider the effect of increasing the number of lanes from two to three in a freeway system. If one had a model of the system in a suitable form and described its performance with two lanes, then with three lanes, and perhaps with four lanes, he could determine the sensitivity of component or system performance to the number of lanes. It is intuitively apparent that a single lane to carry traffic in one direction on a freeway would work extremely poorly; two lanes would effect a great improvement; the third lane would produce a significant improvement if traffic were heavy. But it is doubtful that increasing the number of lanes to six or eight would produce proportionate increases in performance, although one could not decide this intuitively but would have to investigate the performance in terms of a suitable model.

The performance of a component or system is sometimes very

sensitive to the value of one parameter and quite insensitive to that of another. This is important information in the design of a system. If performance is insensitive to a parameter, very little can be accomplished by changing it, whereas if performance is very sensitive to a particular parameter, it can readily be used to improve performance.

The compatibility among components connected together to form a subsystem or a system must be established adequately in the design. The output of one component may be the input of another. If the output of the first is not properly matched to the input of the second component, performance may not be good; in fact, there may be no performance.

An obvious example of this is a system using electric motors. If the motors require 110 volts for operation and if the system voltage is 220 volts, the two are not compatible; an additional component, a transformer, must be inserted to reduce the system voltage and make it compatible with the requirements of the electric motors. In a freeway system a problem of compatibility arises at an intersection of two freeways. In the design of the interchange, provision must be made for the traffic to move off one freeway onto the other. There must be a ramp compatible with the two freeways. It must make possible smooth flow off the one and onto the other. This involves physical considerations, such as grades, curves, sight distances, and the like, and the number of lanes required must be compatible with the density of traffic expected to be changing from one freeway to the other.

One could conceive of a system designed in such a manner that the various elements were compatible, sensitivity had been considered, and, in some sense, the design had been optimized. However, when put in operation, the system might perform in an unstable manner. With some particular input, or indeed with any input, the output might be totally unmanageable. A freeway system could have an off ramp that failed to provide adequate capacity for the traffic. This would result in cars lining up behind the off ramp. This, in turn, would cause a slowdown in the main stream of traffic, which would back up on the freeway. In fact, a wave effect is recognized in situations such as this, and traffic flow may come to a standstill upstream of the off ramp. In this case, the output simply goes to a zero value when the input exceeds a certain number. The ideal system behaves in a stable manner regardless of the input. This cannot be obtained economically in all practical cases. One designs, therefore, to obtain stability under operating conditions likely to be encountered a reasonable proportion of the time. The degree of stability designed into a system depends upon considerations of economics and safety. The damage resulting from instability must be weighed against the cost of obtaining a more stable operation.

5.7. Mathematical Tools

For the successful use of a mathematical model, one must have available the mathematical means for describing the inputs and the relationships between outputs and inputs of the system, as well as mathematical tools for solving the equations constituting the mathematical model. In the following sections, consideration will be given to the mathematical tools necessary to describe inputs that can be represented by analytical expressions of a quite elementary type, as well as the tools needed to solve problems that can be handled by straightforward analysis. Complexities due to the nature of the input will be described, and the use of probability methods for the description of inputs will be considered. The need for numerical solution of some problems will be discussed and illustrated.

The first-order linear differential equation occurs frequently in engineering work. It can be solved readily without recourse to advanced techniques. This equation includes derivatives of the first order only, and the dependent variables appear to the first power only; thus,

$$\frac{dy}{dx} + ay = 0 \tag{5.15}$$

where dy/dx is the derivative of y with respect to x, the rate at which y changes with respect to x for all values of x.

A solution of the equation is

$$y = Ce^{-ax} \tag{5.16}$$

That the expression (5.16) is indeed a solution of Eq. (5.15) can be demonstrated readily. If we differentiate y with respect to x, using the expression for y shown in Eq. (5.16), we obtain the following:

$$\frac{dy}{dx} = -Cae^{-ax} \tag{5.17}$$

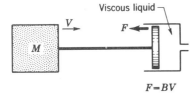

Viscous liquid

$F = BV$

Fig. 5.10 Mass-damping system.

We now substitute this value of dy/dx in Eq. (5.15) and, in addition, substitute the value of y given in (5.16) for y in (5.15) and obtain

$$-Cae^{-ax} + Cae^{-ax} = 0$$

which is an identity. In other words, (5.16) is an expression, in terms of x, that is a solution of the differential equation (5.15). We have not shown that this is the only solution of this problem, but it certainly is a solution and will be used in our ensuing discussions.

An assembly of two mechanical elements shown in Fig. 5.10 can be described by a first-order linear differential equation that will predict performance. The system in Fig. 5.10 consists of a mass and a damping mechanism. The latter generates a frictional force opposing the motion. If the mass and damper are connected by a rigid rod and the system is in motion, this motion can be described by the following equation:

$$M\frac{dV}{dt} + BV = 0 \tag{5.18}$$

where t is the time measured from some initial instant. This is again an application of Newton's second law. It is quite obviously a first-order linear differential equation. The solution is

$$V = Ce^{-(B/M)t} \tag{5.19}$$

Another system, consisting of two mechanical elements, which is within our province, consists of a spring that exerts a force proportional to displacement x and a damping mechanism. Its motion is described by

$$B\frac{dx}{dt} + Kx = 0 \tag{5.20}$$

This again is a linear first-order differential equation, solution of which is

$$x = Ce^{-(K/B)t} \tag{5.21}$$

If we consider the combination of a spring, mass, and damping mechanism and write the equation describing its performance, we no longer have a first-order equation but rather a second-order differential equation, since the acceleration appears and is a second derivative. The solution of this equation was given earlier as Eq. (5.3). It will be discussed for a special case in Sec. 5.8 and more generally in Sec. 7.3.

5.8. Deterministic Inputs

The motion of a particle under the influence of forces can be used to illustrate the mathematical problems involved in formulating a mathematical model, as shown in the previous section. Only in extremely idealized cases can solutions as simple as this be obtained. However, two of these problems will illustrate the points under discussion. We consider first a mathematical model that makes use of elementary analytical tools to describe the input and the motion of a mass.

Returning, now, to the system of Fig. 5.10, a mass and a damping mechanism, shown as a free body in Fig. 5.11, we place this system in motion by, for example, a sharp hammer blow. Initially the mass will have a velocity V_0. Since the rod connecting

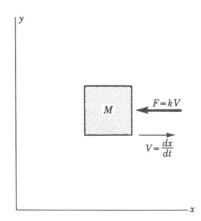

Fig. 5.11   Force-mass system.

mass and damper is rigid, the damping mechanism tends to reduce the velocity of the mass. In accordance with the previous analysis, we write the equation for the system,

$$M \frac{dV}{dt} + BV = 0 \tag{5.18}$$

and the solution,

$$V = Ce^{-(B/M)t} \tag{5.19}$$

Since the velocity is V_0 at $t = 0$, we write

$$V_0 = Ce^0$$

or, since $e^0 = 1$,

$$V_0 = C$$

and finally,

$$V = V_0 e^{-(B/M)t} \tag{5.22}$$

This provides a great deal of information concerning the motion of the mass and the damping mechanism. From simply intuitive considerations it is not obvious exactly how the mass will slow down under the influence of the viscous damping force. The solution of this equation, using the boundary condition that at time zero the velocity is equal to V_0, makes clear that, as time increases, velocity decreases but that, no matter how long the time may be, the velocity never quite equals zero. We find, therefore, that theoretically, in the ideal case presented here, the mass with an initial velocity V_0 would move for an infinite time.

We proceed now to the determination of the distance through which the mass will move after the application of the force that gave it an initial velocity of V_0. If it continues to move under the influence of the damping mechanism, it will move for an infinite time, but it is not necessarily true that it will move an infinite distance. Consider, then, the analysis of this motion, using the previous equation:

$$V = V_0 e^{-(B/M)t} \tag{5.22}$$

Rewriting in terms of the distance x from the initial position,

$$V = \frac{dx}{dt} = V_0 e^{-(B/M)t} \tag{5.23}$$

Rearranging terms,

$$dx = V_0 e^{-(Bt/M)} dt$$

Solving this by integrating both sides, we obtain

$$x = -V_0 \frac{M}{B} e^{-(Bt/M)} + C_1$$

Now if $x = 0$ at $t = 0$, we see that

$$0 = \frac{-V_0 M}{B} e^0 + C_1$$

or $C_1 = \frac{V_0 M}{B}$

Substituting this value for C_1 in the expression for x,

$$x = -\frac{V_0 M}{B} e^{-(Bt/M)} + \frac{V_0 M}{B}$$

or $x = \frac{V_0 M}{B} [1 - e^{-(Bt/M)}] \tag{5.24}$

It is apparent that the term in brackets approaches the value 1.0 as t increases without limit.   The value of x therefore approaches $V_0 M/B$ as a limit.   Hence, although motion will never stop, the distance traveled is finite.   In fact, the initial momentum MV_0 of the mass is the governing factor in determining the distance moved.

In Fig. 5.12 is shown a mass resting on a frictionless surface,

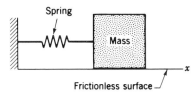

Fig. 5.12   Mass-spring system.

connected to a spring which in turn is connected to a fixed point. If the mass is displaced from its equilibrium position and then released, the spring will exert a force on it and return it toward the equilibrium position. This motion can be described by means of Newton's second law, taking into consideration that the spring exerts a force proportional to its elongation and, in the case of the nomenclature used here, in the direction opposite to the positive value of x. Newton's second law then gives the following equation:

$$M \frac{d^2x}{dt^2} = -Kx \tag{5.25}$$

It is not obvious, but experience has shown that a solution of this equation is the following:

$$x = A \sin \omega t \tag{5.26}$$

This expression for x yields an expression for the velocity, the first derivative of x with respect to the time, as follows:

$$\frac{dx}{dt} = A\omega \cos \omega t$$

Similarly, we obtain an expression for the acceleration, the second derivative of x, as follows:

$$\frac{d^2x}{dt^2} = -A\omega^2 \sin \omega t$$

That the expression for x is indeed a solution of Eq. (5.25) can be shown now by substituting the value for x and the second derivative of x in Eq. (5.25). Following this procedure, we obtain

$$-MA\omega^2 \sin \omega t = -KA \sin \omega t$$

or $\quad (KA - MA\omega^2) \sin \omega t = 0 \tag{5.27}$

This must be true for all values of the time; hence the coefficient $KA - MA\omega^2$ must be zero, and the resulting expression for ω is

$$\omega = \sqrt{\frac{K}{M}}$$

The expression for x in terms of $\sin \omega t$ is a solution of the equation. This means of obtaining solutions is not at all unusual. If intuition leads to a solution of a differential equation, the method is perfectly valid. It does not in any way make a statement that this is the only solution of the equation, nor indeed is it the only solution.

The physical interpretation of Eq. (5.27) is that when the mass is displaced and released it will be pulled in the direction of the negative x axis. This will accelerate the mass, and when it reaches the point $x = 0$, there will be no further force exerted on it, but it will have a momentum equal to the product of the mass and the velocity at that time. This will carry the mass beyond the equilibrium position and, if we assume the spring to be double-acting, will generate a force in the spring, again resisting the motion. This will slow down the mass and ultimately it will come to rest, but at the moment it comes to rest there will be a spring force acting upon it in the direction of the positive x axis equal to the product of K and x. The motion, then, continues indefinitely so long as there is no frictional force acting on the body, which is the assumption made in deriving the equations.

This, then, is an example of a system that can be described by an analytical expression having a solution obtainable by straightforward methods. If the system is a mass, a spring, and a damping force, the combination discussed earlier, it requires more sophisticated methods for the solution of the equation.

We consider, now, a hypothetical case which illustrates certain difficulties due to the nature of the input. Figure 5.13 shows a mass,

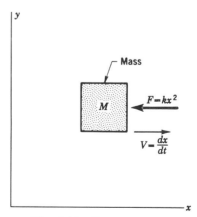

Fig. 5.13 Force-mass system.

moving at a velocity $V = dx/dt$. A force is acting in opposition to the motion of the body, proportional to the square of the distance from some fixed point distance x away. This motion can again be described by Newton's second law; in other words, the mathematical model representing this motion is the same as in each case considered previously. We write, therefore,

$$M \frac{d^2x}{dt^2} = -kx^2 \tag{5.28}$$

This cannot be solved by the elementary analytical methods used above but can be put into a form that lends itself to numerical methods; thus,

$$V = \frac{dx}{dt}$$

and $\quad \dfrac{dV}{dt} = \dfrac{d^2x}{dt^2}$

Now we write $\quad M \dfrac{dV}{dt} = -kx^2$

or $\quad dV = -\dfrac{k}{M} x^2 \, dt \tag{5.29}$

Initial conditions are, at $t = 0$, $x = x_0$ and $V = V_0$. Now the expression for dV in terms of ΔV, a finite increment in V, is as follows:

$$\Delta V = -\frac{k}{M} x^2 \, \Delta t \tag{5.30}$$

After a time Δt has elapsed, the new value of V is V_1; hence,

$$V_1 = V_0 + \Delta V$$

and since, approximately,

$$\Delta x = \frac{V_0 + V_1}{2} \Delta t$$

we have $\quad x_1 = x_0 + \Delta x = x_0 + \dfrac{V_0 + V_1}{2} \Delta t \tag{5.31}$

which gives a new value of x to use in Eq. (5.30) to find new increments ΔV and Δx. We thus proceed, step by step, to the determination of x and V as functions of t and finally V as a function of x.

These are expressions for the velocity and the displacement x in terms of the incremental velocities, times, and distances. We can begin at time zero, assign a value to Δt, compute the corresponding value of ΔV, from that compute a new value of the velocity V_1, proceed to the calculation of the increment in x, Δx, and then the new value of x_1 in terms of x_0 and Δx. We can continue in this manner, securing new values of the displacement and the velocity at the end of successive intervals of time, Δt, until we have progressed as far as desired in the analysis. Figure 5.14 shows the general form of the solution of this equation obtained by numerical means. The velocity decreases as the distance increases and eventually goes to zero. The displacement x is initially x_0 and increases continually until the velocity becomes zero. If we investigate the events of the next interval of time, we note that, since the force opposes the original motion and the velocity has decreased to zero, there will be an acceleration causing a velocity in the direction opposite to the original, which will then cause a decrease in the displacement x. Numerical solution lends itself well to the use of the digital computer, and with a suitable program a solution of this problem can be obtained in a very short time.

These elementary illustrations are only an introduction to the mathematical problems that can be handled analytically in establishing models of physical systems. Great complexity is encountered as

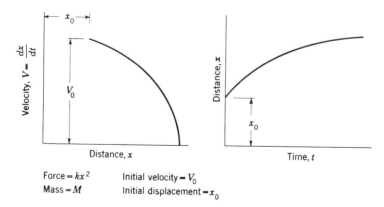

Fig. 5.14 Velocity-distance-time diagrams.

soon as a system becomes anything more than a simple mass particle with springs and dampers.

5.9. Inputs Varying with Time and Place

In the freeway system discussed earlier, it was noted that the inputs to the system, that is, the traffic entering the on ramps, would vary from time to time and place to place. In discussing the elementary feasibility study, we made a very crude assumption that the inputs arose uniformly throughout the area during a period of 90 min. This assumption might be adequate for a preliminary design, but for the detailed design of on ramps, off ramps, interchanges, and the like, more accurate data would be needed. Traffic surveys provide information concerning the distribution of traffic flow at different points in the area and at different times of day and week. These data are in the form of numbers of cars passing a given point at a given time. If there were great regularity in the distribution, it might be possible to set up a simple analytical expression to describe the origin of traffic.

For example, it might be found that at a particular point in the system at 7:30 in the morning there was no traffic and that gradually during the following hour the number of cars passing the point each minute increased linearly with the passage of time. This would make possible an analytical expression for the number of cars as a linear function of the time. On the other hand, the number of cars originating in a particular area could perhaps be expressed as a trigonometric function of the time. This would indicate no traffic at a certain time, increasing gradually to a maximum, and then decreasing to zero again, in the form, perhaps, of a sine curve. This could be used throughout a portion of the cycle only, since the sine has negative values after a half cycle of positive values.

In the case of traffic distribution, it is much more likely that the data representing traffic flow will not be in a form that can be expressed by simple analytical expressions. Traffic flow has a random nature. It becomes necessary, therefore, to make use of the mathematics of probability and statistics to describe suitably the input to a system of this kind.

Systems for customer servicing or, in the case of the military, subject to attack by missiles, planes, or artillery, all require the use of probability methods for a description of the inputs. Since the inputs are distributed more or less randomly through time and perhaps space as well, the outputs of the system will very likely have a similar nature, although the effect of the system may be to change the flow through it so that the output will be quite different from the input. In any case, use of mathematical methods in describing the input and the flow through the system is essential in order to carry out any useful analytical procedures to determine the performance of the system. The methods available for the analysis of inputs and the flow through systems with variable inputs will be described in the following section.

5.10. Probability Methods

Variables that do not lend themselves to description by the analytical means discussed thus far are frequent in system design. These variables, which cannot be described as continuous functions of time or space, occur when inputs to a system are generated randomly or in a manner at least appearing to be random.

A random phenomenon can be defined[1] as an empirical phenomenon, characterized by the property that its observation, under a given set of circumstances, does not always lead to the same observed outcome but rather to different outcomes in such a way that there is statistical regularity. A random event is one whose relative frequency of occurrence in a very long sequence of observations of randomly selected situations in which the event may occur approaches a stable limit value as the number of observations is increased to infinity. The limit value of the relative frequency is called the probability of the random event. The generation of traffic in a city or along a freeway has this characteristic of randomness.

Data relating to phenomena such as the height and weight of human beings, the scores made on a standardized test by students, or the numbers appearing on a pair of dice that have been tossed fairly describe variables whose distribution is shown in Fig. 5.15. The vertical bars are the number of items occurring within the interval represented on the abscissa. The curve passing through the high points of the bars represents an analytical expression that can be

[1] Emanuel Parzen, "Modern Probability Theory and Its Application," p. 2, John Wiley & Sons, Inc., New York, 1960.

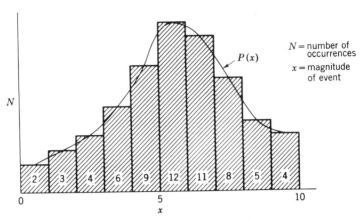

Fig. 5.15 Frequency-distribution representation.

used to describe the distribution indicated by the solid bars. This is called a probability distribution. Analytically, it is expressed as $P(x)$. In this context, $P(x)$ is the number of occurrences of x of magnitude greater than x and less than $x + dx$ divided by the total number of occurrences of x.

In Fig. 5.15 there are eight occurrences of events having a value of x larger than 7 but less than 8. The total number of events called x with values between 0 and 10 is 64. The probability distribution $P(x)$ for x in this interval is 8 divided by 64. Similarly, the probability distribution $P(x)$ for items with a value greater than 2 but less than 3, of which there are four shown in Fig. 5.15, is $\frac{4}{64}$ or $\frac{1}{16}$.

The mean value of a variable x is denoted by μ and is defined by

$$\mu = \sum_{x=-\infty}^{\infty} xP(x) \tag{5.32}$$

Let us consider the rolling of two dice. The dice are each six-sided and have the numbers 1 to 6 on the various faces. The dice are fair dice, and the probability of any number appearing is equal to that of any other on each die. Let n be the number of independent rolls of the dice, and p be the probability of a single pertinent event: for example, the rolling of a 6 on each of the dice. Let k be the number of successful events, or pertinent events. It is desired to determine the probability of obtaining k successes in n independent trials, or rolls of the dice, for example, of obtaining three rolls of 7 in ten rolls of the dice. The quantity p^k is the probability that the first k rolls will be successes. In the example, p^3 is the probability that the first three rolls of the dice will be 7s. The probability that the succeeding seven trials will not be successful is $(1 - p)^{(n-k)}$. The quantity $q = 1 - p$ is the probability that a trial will not be successful. The number of unsuccessful trials will, of course, be the difference between the total number of trials and the successful trials.

However, there are many different ways in which these events could occur. It is not necessary that the first three trials be successful and the succeeding seven unsuccessful; rather, the three successful trials could be distributed throughout the ten trials in a large number of different ways. Each one of these will supply a satisfactory result. The number of ways that this can occur is described by considering the number of combinations of n things taken k at a time. We shall denote this by C_k^n, and its value is given by

$$C_k^n = \frac{n!}{k!(n - k)!} \tag{5.33}$$

If we multiply the number of combinations of n things, taken k at a time, by the probability that three trials will be successful and seven trials will be unsuccessful, the final expression for the probability that exactly k, or, in this case, three trials out of ten, will be successful is

$$p(k) = \frac{n!}{k!(n - k)!} p^k q^{(n-k)} \tag{5.34}$$

This equation describes the probability of obtaining k successes in n trials, where the events are characterized by the same features as the rolling of dice; namely, the number n is finite, k is an integer, and each roll of the dice or each event is completely independent of each preceding or following event. A distribution such as this one is known as a binomial or Bernoulli distribution. Equation (5.34) describes the situation adequately, provided the assumptions are fulfilled.

An approximation to this equation can be obtained under certain circumstances. If the number n is very large and k is very small compared with n, the quantity $n!/(n - k)!$ would contain only the larger terms $n(n - 1)$, $(n - 2)$, etc. Since n is large compared with k, these larger terms would each be approximately equal to n, and there would be precisely k of these terms, since the terms in $n!$ that are common to $(n - k)!$ would cancel in numerator and denominator. This leaves approximately n^k for $n!/(n - k)!$. The expression for $p(k)$ then reads

$$p(k) \cong \frac{n^k}{k!} p^k q^n \tag{5.35}$$

Since $q = 1 - p$, and for the product np we write μ, the equation becomes

$$p(k) \cong \frac{\mu^k}{k!} (1 - p)^n \tag{5.36}$$

Now if n is very large, the quantity p is small and the expansion of the quantity $(1 - p)^n$ is approximately $1 - np$. Furthermore, e^x is approximately $1 + x$, or e^{-x} is approximately $1 - x$. We can then substitute for $1 - np$ the quantity e^{-np}. Finally, then, for an approximate form of the equation, we have

$$p(k) \cong \frac{\mu^k}{k!} e^{-\mu} \tag{5.37}$$

This approximation to the binomial distribution is known as the Poisson distribution. It is adequate provided that the number n is large and k is small compared with n. In addition, the variable can take on only integral values, as was the case with the binomial distribution. However, the mean of the distribution need not be an integral value.

If the distribution is continuous and not discrete, it may be described by an equation known as the normal distribution, which is given by

$$P(x) = \frac{1}{\sqrt{2\pi}\,\sigma} e^{-(x-\mu)^2/2\sigma^2}$$

Here the quantity μ is the mean value of x, and σ, the standard deviation, will be defined in the following discussion.

Each of these distributions has a characteristic in common;

namely, the integral of $P(x)\ dx$ between $-\infty$ and $+\infty$ is equal to 1.0.

The variance of a distribution, defined by σ^2, is a measure of the dispersion of the variable; that is, all the values of a distribution with a small value of σ^2 would be closely centered around the mean value, whereas in a distribution with a large value of σ^2 the values of the variable extend over a wide range compared with the magnitude of the mean value of the variable itself. The square root of the variance, σ, is called the standard deviation. The quantities σ^2 and σ are defined by the expression

$$\sigma^2 = \sum_{x=-\infty}^{\infty} \left\{ \left[x - \sum_{x=-\infty}^{\infty} xP(x) \right]^2 P(x) \right\} = \sum_{x=-\infty}^{\infty} (x - \mu)^2 (Px)$$

$$(5.38)$$

If a distribution is given in terms of its mean value and its standard deviation, a great deal is known about the distribution. This accounts partially for the importance of the quantities mean and standard deviation and the necessity for their definitions at this time.

The significance of the mean and the variance and the use of the equations defining them can be illustrated by two examples. In the first example, the variable x, which ranges in magnitude between 1 and 20, has the frequency distribution shown in Table 5.1. To illustrate the meaning of the distribution, we note that values of

Table 5.1

Interval	x_{av}	N	$P(x)$	$xP(x)$	$x - \mu$	$(x - \mu)^2$	$(x - \mu)^2 P(x)$
1–2	1.5	2	0.02	0.030	−9	81	1.62
3–4	3.5	5	0.05	0.175	−7	49	2.45
5–6	5.5	9	0.09	0.495	−5	25	1.75
7–8	7.5	14	0.14	1.050	−3	9	1.26
9–10	9.5	20	0.20	1.900	−1	1	0.20
11–12	11.5	20	0.20	2.300	1	1	0.20
13–14	13.5	14	0.14	1.890	3	9	1.26
15–16	15.5	9	0.09	1.395	5	25	1.75
17–18	17.5	5	0.05	0.875	7	49	2.45
19–20	19.5	2	0.02	0.390	9	81	1.62
$\Sigma =$	. . .	100	1.00	10.500	. . .	. . .	14.56
	$\mu = 10.5$		$\sigma^2 = 14.56$		$\sigma = 3.81$		

$x = 9$ or 10 occur 20 times out of a total of 100 values of x. Also, values of $x = 5$ and 6 occur 9 times per 100. We note also that the distribution is symmetrical. In other words, the values 3 and 4 occur the same number of times as 17 and 18.

The mean value of x is computed by the following procedure. The relative frequency of each interval, $P(x)$, is calculated from the relationship

$$P(x) = \frac{N}{\Sigma N}$$

The weighted value of each item of the tabulation is then calculated by multiplying the average value of x in each interval by $P(x)$, as shown in the fifth column of the tabulation. The total of all values of $xP(x)$ is the mean value μ as defined previously:

$$\mu = \sum_{x-\infty}^{\infty} xP(x)$$

The deviation of each interval from the mean, $x - \mu$, is shown in the sixth column. The square of this deviation is in the seventh column, and the next column tabulates the values of $(x - \mu)^2 P(x)$. The variance σ^2 is given by

$$\sigma^2 = \Sigma(x - \mu)^2 P(x)$$

and is the sum of the quantities in the eighth column. The standard deviation σ is the square root of this quantity; hence

$$\sigma = \sqrt{\Sigma(x - \mu)^2 P(x)}$$

The nature of this distribution is shown graphically in Fig. 5.16. The standard deviation is indicated as a distance in units of x from the mean.

In Table 5.2, or Fig. 5.17, a somewhat different distribution function is shown. In this case, the mean is the same as in the case of Table 5.1 and Fig. 5.16. However, the relatively greater frequency of large and small numbers compared with the mean results in a larger measure of the dispersion $\sigma = 4.83$, compared with 3.81 of the first case.

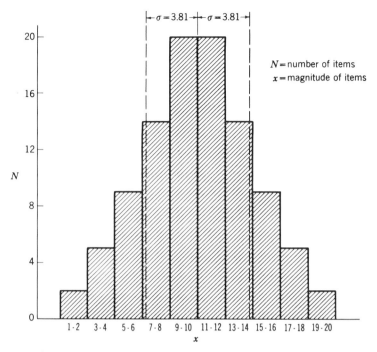

Fig. 5.16 Frequency distribution with small standard deviation.

Table 5.2

Interval	x_{av}	N	$P(x)$	$xP(x)$	$x - \mu$	$(x - \mu)^2$	$(x - \mu)^2 P(x)$
1–2	1.5	5	0.05	0.075	9	81	4.05
3–4	3.5	8	0.08	0.280	7	49	3.92
5–6	5.5	10	0.10	0.550	5	25	2.50
7–8	7.5	12	0.12	0.900	3	9	1.08
9–10	9.5	15	0.15	1.425	1	1	0.15
11–12	11.5	15	0.15	1.725	1	1	0.15
13–14	13.5	12	0.12	1.620	3	9	1.08
15–16	15.5	10	0.10	1.550	5	25	2.50
17–18	17.5	8	0.08	1.400	7	49	3.92
19–20	19.5	5	0.05	0.975	9	81	4.05
$\Sigma =$	...	100	1.00	10.500	...	...	23.40

$$\mu = 10.5 \qquad \sigma^2 = 23.40 \qquad \sigma = 4.83$$

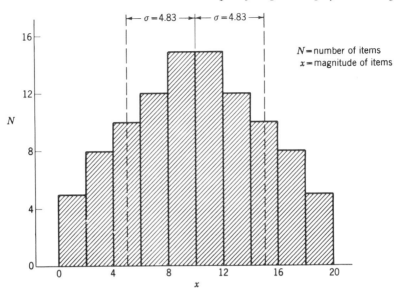

Fig. 5.17   Frequency distribution with large standard deviation.

An application of probability methods in a problem in queueing theory is illustrated beginning in Fig. 5.18.   Here is shown a familiar situation in which customers approaching a service counter are the input *I*.   The output is serviced customers leaving the counter. The counter is the service channel, as noted in Fig. 5.18.   This might be a counter at a supermarket, a station in a factory assembly line, a ticket office at an airline center, or any other area in which people or physical objects are directed to a center, serviced there, and dispatched from this center.

In order to describe the events occurring at such a counter or channel in mathematical form, it is necessary to describe two features of these circumstances: first, the number of inputs that occur in any given time and, second, the rate at which service is given to the customers.   If we are able to formulate these two features of the servicing center, it is possible to predict performance.   For example, it is intuitively obvious that, if the inputs arrive so frequently that the

Fig. 5.18   Block diagram of service counter.

servicing cannot take care of them, a queue, or waiting line, will form. If the inputs arrive at a constant rate and the service is at a constant rate, the solution of the problem is very simple. If the mean number of inputs per unit time to the system is m, and the mean number of outputs per unit time when the channel is occupied is M, and if n is the queue length, that is, the number of customers standing in line, including those who are in the channel for service, and if, as stated above, the rate of service is constant and the rate of arrival is constant, we may write

$$(m - M)t = n \tag{5.39}$$

where t is the interval of time since the line began to form. This simply states a conservation principle. The number of people in the waiting line is equal to the number of people arriving per unit time, minus the number of people being serviced per unit time, multiplied by the time during which this process has been going on, since all customers must be accounted for. If the rate of service, M, is greater than the rate of input, the equation is meaningless, since there would be a negative number of people in the waiting line; we interpret this to mean no line would form. If m and M are equal, then there will never be a waiting line. If, on the other hand, $m > M$, there will always be a waiting line, and it will continuously grow in magnitude.

In a real situation, it is extremely unlikely that the inputs would occur at a constant rate. It is necessary, therefore, to describe the variability of the input. We would expect that the inputs to any situation would be statistically distributed in some manner, except in a factory where the assembly line requires a constant, or nearly constant, rate of input. That is, we could expect a larger number of customers for a portion of the time, a smaller number at other times, etc. If we were to plot the expected number of arrivals at the input in a given period of time against the frequency with which we would expect this number of arrivals to occur, we would obtain a diagram such as Fig. 5.19. Neither a very large number of arrivals nor a very small number occurs very often. Further, the expectation of no arrivals is small. It is probable that an intermediate number of arrivals will occur most of the time.

If the holding time, that is, the time required to service a customer, is a constant, the nature of the waiting line will depend upon

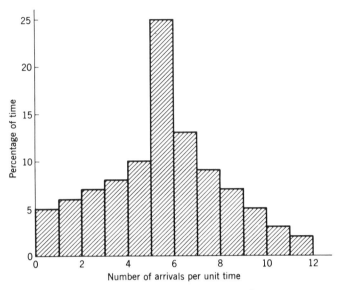

Fig. 5.19   Frequency diagram of customer arrivals.

the distribution of the inputs.   Quite obviously, no line will form if the number of inputs arriving in a given time is less than the number of customers that can be serviced.

To examine the effect of the manner in which inputs arrive, we shall consider a case in which the arrivals are described by a Poisson distribution; thus,

$$p(r) = \frac{e^{-mT}(mT)^r}{r!} \tag{5.40}$$

where $p(r)$ is the probability that exactly r inputs will arrive in a given time; m is the mean number of inputs arriving per unit time; T is time; r is the number of inputs arriving in a given period.   The Poisson distribution applies in this case if the number of inputs in a given interval is small compared with the total number of inputs in a day.   Since the mean number of inputs per unit time is m and the holding time per customer is T, the product mT is the mean number of customers that arrive while one customer is being served.   The probability that r customers will arrive while one customer is served is $p(r)$.   The holding time T may be either constant or variable and Eq. (5.40) is valid.

Let us assume that the time required to service one customer is 1 min. We also assume that the average number of arrivals for service is at the rate of one per minute. Using the following equation to compute the probability of various numbers of arrivals in a given period of time, we see the results in Table 5.3.

$$p(r) = \frac{e^{-mT}(mT)^r}{r!}$$

The first column is the number of inputs per minute, the second column is the factorial of the first column, and the third column is the probability that exactly r arrivals will occur per minute. The fourth column represents the probable number of minutes per day of 10 hr during which the number of arrivals of the first column may be expected.

For example, zero arrivals per minute is expected 0.367 per cent of the time, or about 220 min. Six or more arrivals per minute is not expected to occur more than 1 min per day; hence we need not consider these in this preliminary analysis, although it must be realized that there is a finite possibility that as many as 20 might arrive for service in a given minute. This would not be likely to occur very often, but it could occur. During the periods when no one arrives for service and one per minute arrives, no waiting line would form. When two or more arrive per minute, there will be a waiting line. We note that during 440 min of a 600-min day, no

Table 5.3

r	$r!$	$p(r)$	Minutes per day	Customers
0	1	0.367	220	0
1	1	0.367	220	220
2	2	0.183	110	220
3	6	0.061	37	111
4	24	0.015	9	36
5	120	0.0031	2	10
6	720	5.1×10^{-4}		
8	40,320	9.1×10^{-6}		
10	3.62×10^6	1.01×10^{-7}		

difficulty will be encountered.   However, during the remaining 160 min of the day, as indicated in the last column of the table, there will be 20 arrivals at the rate of two per minute, 111 at the rate of three, 36 at the rate of four, and 10 at the rate of five—a total of 377 arrivals in a period of only 158 min.   Quite obviously, there will be waiting lines during a considerable portion of the day.

It is interesting to consider the unlikely assumption that during the first 220 min no one would arrive for service and during the next 220 min, one person would arrive per minute.   So far no difficulty would have been experienced, but from then on, as the rate of arrivals continued to increase, the line would continue to grow; at the end of the working day there would be 219 people in line waiting to be served.   The last series of events is extremely unlikely, but it could happen.

In order to compute the expected length of the waiting line under the circumstances described here, more sophisticated methods are required.   These will not be presented in this discussion.   However, one further example will be cited to clarify the concepts involved.   We make a slight change in the data for the problem, servicing one customer per minute, as before, at each counter but installing an additional counter so that, on an average, a customer arrives every 2 min, that is, the average number of customers per minute is 0.5.   Under these circumstances, as shown in Table 5.4, conditions are somewhat better than before.

The fact that only 300 customers will arrive for service at each counter during a 600-min day would at first indicate that there should be no waiting line at any time.   However, we note that during 54

Table 5.4

r	$r!$	$(mT)^r$	$p(r)$	Minutes per day	Customers
0	1	1	0.606	364	0
1	1	0.5	0.303	182	182
2	2	0.25	0.076	45	90
3	6	0.125	0.013	8	24
4	24	0.062	0.0016	1	4
					300

min of the day one would expect more customers to arrive than could be serviced, as shown in the fifth column of Table 5.4. Customers arrive at the rate of two per minute for 45 min, three per minute for 8 min, and four per minute for 1 min, giving a total of 118 customers in a period of 54 min. If the distribution of these arrivals should happen to be, as indicated in the previous discussion, no one for the first 364 min, one for the next 182 min, and then, during the following 55 min, 118 arrivals, we should have, at the end of the working day, a waiting line of 64 people. This is the worst condition that could be postulated for a simple analysis of this sort, and we note that conditions are very much improved in the second case, although at a very considerable price. Facilities have been doubled, and we still cannot be absolutely certain that we can take care of the problem.

In a real situation, it would be necessary to calculate the costs of providing better service and to compare them with the costs of waiting lines. The analysis above is too elementary to provide the data to make such a decision.

We have interpreted probabilities in terms of minutes. When we had a probability of 0.303, as we had in the second case for one arrival per minute, we say that this will occur during 182 min of the day. This is not exactly the proper way to interpret this, although, over a long period of time, it would work out in this manner. Rather, we would say that there is approximately a 30 per cent chance, at any time during the day, that the arrivals will be at the rate of one per minute and that there is a 0.0016 chance at any time that the arrivals will be at the rate of four per minute. This percentage chance of arrival and its conversion into minutes during which these arrivals will take place must not be misinterpreted to mean that every day the traffic will be the same.

Furthermore, it is impossible to say in what order these people will arrive for service. We consider two arbitrary schemes to illustrate the effect of the order of arrival. These are shown in Fig. 5.20. The first assumes no arrivals for service before the end of 363 min and that they then arrive in increasing numbers, as described earlier. There is no waiting line until 545 min have elapsed, and the day ends with 64 customers in line.

The second scheme assumes that arrivals are in the reversed order, that is, the heavy requests for service come first; we show this

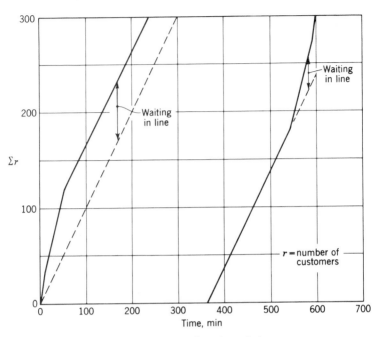

Fig. 5.20   Customer servicing as a function of time.

at the left end of the plotting.   Here, during the first minute, four customers arrive for service and one is serviced.   During the next 8 min, 24 arrive and 8 are serviced.   During the next 45 min, 92 arrive and 45 are serviced.   At the end of this rush period we again have a waiting line of 64 customers, and this number in line continues until the end of 237 min, during the last 182 min of which there is a constant waiting line and arrival of customers is exactly equal to the servicing.   At the end of 300 min all the customers have been serviced, and the last customer in line would have waited over an hour.

With the specified parameters of the system, actual conditions would not be likely to be as bad as either of the situations just described.   In each case, periods during which no one arrives for service have been concentrated.   Such would not be the case, and the length of the waiting line would be very much less than the 64 shown in each of these cases.   Since there is a 61 per cent probability of no one arriving in any given minute, only a very unfortunate combination of circumstances would result in a waiting line exceeding 10 customers.

Although it is beyond the scope of the present discussion, it can be shown that, if the ratio of mean arrivals to mean services per unit time is $\rho = m/M$, then the number of customers, N, to be expected in the waiting line is given by

$$N = \rho + \frac{\rho^2}{2(1 - \rho)} \tag{5.41}$$

In the second case discussed above, where $m = 0.5$ and $M = 1$, and hence $\rho = 0.5$, the expected length of waiting line, from Eq. (5.41), is

$$N = 0.5 + \frac{0.5^2}{2(1 - 0.5)}$$

$$N = 0.5 + 0.25 = 0.75$$

It is anticipated that under these circumstances the waiting line will have less than one customer, on an average. If $\rho = 1$, the denominator of Eq. (5.41) is zero; hence the waiting line grows without limit, as in the case discussed above.

If much greater complexity were introduced into the problem, the analytical procedures would become more intractable. For example, a not very complex set of circumstances would include a number of servicing channels, several sources of inputs, and means for funneling the various inputs from the various sources into the individual channels.

In practice, there are several complicating features. If the waiting line for one channel becomes excessively long, the customers will tend to change lines, thereby in a sense equalizing the length of the lines waiting at the various channels. Under certain circumstances, the customer may not have control over the waiting line into which he will go. This is characteristic of the telephone system where, if the circuits are busy, waiting customers are selected at random. In traffic control, even greater complexity enters the problem. Each street intersection is comparable to a servicing area such as we have just considered. Decisions controlling the direction in which a car will turn are made by individuals but must be expressed analytically. If there are more than half a dozen or so intersections, it is easy to see that the analytical difficulties will soon outstrip the ability to handle them.   Therefore, some other method of analyzing these problems is needed.

The use of numerical methods to analyze problems of great complexity and difficulty suggests itself, by analogy with the use of numerical methods to solve intractable differential equations.   Such problems were hinted at in the preceding section.   They do not lend themselves to analytical solutions in the manner of the problem of the single service channel.   For purposes of illustration, numerical methods will be used to suggest a method of solution for the problem just discussed.   The inputs to the servicing center were statistically distributed, as illustrated in Tables 5.3 and 5.4.   The analytical model used was the Poisson distribution; this approximates very closely, particularly for large numbers, the normal or gaussian, which represents quite accurately many distributions in nature.

In using numerical methods, one substitutes for the analytical expression a numerical model that will provide an indication of the distribution of inputs with time.   A number of methods are available for accomplishing this end, and we shall discuss two of them.   The inputs to our system can be represented by using a pair of dice.   We assume that the average number of customers expected over a period of time is seven.   This is the average number obtained when throwing a pair of dice.   If we were to throw a pair of dice a fairly large number of times, for example, a hundred times, and record the frequency with which the various combinations appeared, we would have a random list that could be used to describe the inputs to our system.   If we did this, we would discover that the possible number combinations from 2 to 12 occurred with approximately the following frequencies:

Number combinations	Frequency, %
2 and 12	2.78
3 and 11	5.55
4 and 10	8.33
5 and 9	11.11
6 and 8	13.90
7	16.66

Throwing dice to determine the input to our system would be a possibility but not a particularly practical one.   A much more suitable method of obtaining the same end is to use a table of random numbers.   A table of 1,000 random numbers, from 000 to 999, could be used in the following manner.   We divide the random numbers into groups that are proportional in size to the percentage of times that we expect each of the digits from 2 to 12 to appear, as follows:

2	0–27
3	28–82
4	83–165
5	166–276
6	277–415
7	416–582
8	583–721
9	722–832
10	833–916
11	917–971
12	972–999

We consult the random list in order and, as the numbers appear, we assign the appropriate number from 2 to 12; this becomes our new list of randomly distributed inputs of magnitude 2 through 12.   In an actual case, we might include the numbers 0 and 1; we could do this by using the numbers 0 through 10, rather than those 2 through 12, and assign the same intervals in the random-number table.   In any case, we should finally have, for the input, a series of numbers that would be distributed in the manner decided upon as reasonable. A similar technique could be used to determine the length of the holding time.   If the holding time were, on an average, 2 min and had a standard deviation of 1 min, that is, approximately 68 per cent of all holding times lie between 1 and 3 min, we could establish a series of numbers corresponding to holding times.   However, in this case it would be better to establish a series of numbers corresponding to the number of services rendered per unit time.   With such a series at hand, we could then solve the problem in the following manner.

A number would be selected corresponding to the number of inputs in the first unit of time.   Then a number would be selected representing the number of services rendered during the first period of time.   The number of inputs, minus the number of services, is the number still left in the waiting line at the end of the first period.   A new number is selected for inputs and a new number for services; the number in the waiting line is increased by the number of inputs and decreased by the number of services. We continue in this manner until a suitable length of time has been covered to establish reasonably what might be expected of the service channel.

Quite obviously, this would be a very tedious task to perform by hand, and once again the computer comes into the picture as the best means for carrying out the procedure. The computer would be supplied with a list of random numbers and the directions for carrying out the summation of inputs, number of services, and determination of waiting-line length. This analysis could be carried out in a very short time compared with the actual time that would be consumed in the servicing procedure itself. If, as we assumed, 2 min were required, on an average, for servicing an individual customer, the computer could simulate the same thing in a very small fraction of a second. We could then easily investigate an entire week's operation of a servicing center in a period of certainly less than an hour on the computer. This would be far too simple a problem to warrant large expenditures for the use of a computer. However, a very slight complication of the setup would justify its use in comparison with any other possible method of solving the problem.

5.11. Sources of Data

In Secs. 5.1 to 5.10, we have discussed the use of mathematical models and techniques to analyze and predict the performance of a system or components of a system. In all cases, we assumed that there would be available suitable data describing the parameters of the system. Securing data is frequently one of the most difficult aspects of system design.

Physical data to describe the systems to be analyzed can be obtained by experiments on a component to determine the relationships between input and output. However, frequently the relationships are not quite as unambiguous as was indicated in the examples earlier in this chapter. It is not always expedient to build even the components in order to determine the coefficients to be used; hence it becomes necessary to select certain values of the constants from previous knowledge or from basic physical laws, extending these to more complex situations. In any case, there is the problem of choosing a suitable value for a constant in an equation describing a set of physical circumstances, and one must resort to whatever means are at his disposal to make certain that the value is the best obtainable under the circumstances. If there is doubt concerning the values used, one must then, in a final interpretation of the results of the analysis, take cognizance of this fact and estimate what effect on final performance a variation of one or all of the parameters might have. One of the favorable aspects of system design is that wide variations in some of the parameters frequently do not cause significant changes in the overall performance obtained.

In the case of probability models, the sources of data can be questionable to a serious degree. For example, in the very elementary case of customer servicing in a single channel, it would be necessary to determine something about the expected number of customers in a given interval and the variation of this number over an extended period of time. Previously established similar customer-servicing areas would be good sources of data, but it would be essential to observe, for a fairly long time, the number of arrivals at a customer-servicing center and to reduce the data so obtained to usable numbers. Transferability of these data to a new center would require thorough consideration and evaluation to establish its validity. In the absence of such data, the selection of numbers in an arbitrary manner requires great experience and background to avoid embarrassing failures. The collection of data brings to the fore the necessity for experimental design and the development of a technique in experimentation; this, of course, is not a new concept but rather one of long standing in component design and testing.

Problems

Describe each of the following systems by means of a block diagram and a mathematical model. Solve the equations and interpret the solution in physical terms.

5.1. A chemical process requires a 1,000-gal tank for mixing and storing two materials. The tank must be 5 ft in diameter, and the volume must be maintained within ± 15 gal of the 1,000-gal quantity. Two materials flow into the tank, one at a temperature of 100°F and the other at a temperature of 180°F. The mixture must be maintained at a temperature of 140°F plus or minus 2°.

5.2. A traffic intersection between highway 1 going north and highway 2 going east, each carrying one-way traffic only, has traffic densities as follows: Northbound on highway 1 between 7 and 9 o'clock in the morning, traffic increases uniformly from zero to 100 cars per minute. Between 9 o'clock and noon, traffic decreases uniformly from 100 cars per minute to no perceptible flow at noon. Eastbound, on highway 2, between 7 and 8 in the morning, traffic increases uniformly from no flow to 50 cars per minute and between 8 o'clock and noon decreases uniformly from 50 cars per minute to no perceptible flow. At the intersection it has been observed that one-half of the traffic northbound on highway 1 turns right onto highway 2, and one-half goes straight through. On highway 2, one-fourth of the traffic turns left to the northbound lanes on highway 1, and three-quarters goes straight ahead.

5.3. At a service counter, the demand for service during the day increases from zero at opening time to a maximum at mid-day and then drops off to zero at the end of the day, in accordance with the expression

$$D = D_0 \sin^2 \theta$$

where $\theta = 2\pi T/10$ and T is the time in hours between opening and the instant under consideration. The rate of service at the counter is a constant.

5.4. Traffic at the intersection of two one-way streets is controlled by a traffic light. Consider the situation with traffic so heavy in both directions that each time the light turns red cars line up to such a distance that traffic is not cleared by the green light before the light turns red again. In the mathematical model, consider the reaction time of drivers in starting their cars and the spacing between cars when in motion.

5.5. A service counter has three channels. Demand remains constant throughout the day. Service time varies. Customers change from one line to another when the line in which they find themselves is more than two customers longer than one of the adjacent lines.

References

Asimow, Morris: "Introduction to Design," pp. 73–84, Prentice-Hall, Inc., Englewood Cliffs, N.J., 1962.

Blackburn, J. F., G. Reethof, and J. L. Shearer: "Fluid Power Control," pp. 96–114, John Wiley & Sons, Inc., New York, 1960.

Goode, H. H., and R. E. Machol: "System Engineering," pp. 58–116, 131–143, McGraw-Hill Book Company, New York, 1957.

Lynch, W. A., and J. G. Truxal, "Signals and Systems in Electrical Engineering," pp. 65–215, 285–341, McGraw-Hill Book Company, New York, 1962.

———— and ————: "Principles of Electronic Instrumentation," pp. 552–562, McGraw-Hill Book Company, New York, 1962.

———— and ————: "Introductory System Analysis," McGraw-Hill Book Company, New York, 1961.

Parzen, Emanuel: "Modern Probability Theory and Its Application," John Wiley & Sons, Inc., New York, 1960.

Raven, Francis H.: "Automatic Control Engineering," pp. 207–238, McGraw-Hill Book Company, New York, 1961.

Tools of Optimization

6.1. Criteria The quality of the performance of a system is fixed in the process of optimization. Optimization of design means that performance or cost or some other measure of its quality has been brought to a point such that it meets the criteria as well as any design could or that is the best possible. In order to make the statement that a system has been optimized, a criterion must have been established to determine the quality of the design in this particular respect. If no criterion is established, no statement can be made concerning the excellence of a design.

We can illustrate this point in a very elementary manner. A particular system incorporates an electric motor to drive a mechanical element. Certain facts have been ascertained as follows: The cost of electric motors increases as their efficiency increases. The cost of electrical energy is a fixed amount per unit of energy. The life of the motor is independent of the cost.

The total cost of the electric motor and of the energy required to drive it during its life is a criterion that can be used to measure the quality of this element of the system. The best selection of a motor would be the one minimizing the total cost of the motor and energy, since it has been observed that the life of the motor does not

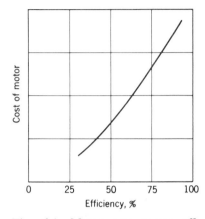

Fig. 6.1 Motor cost versus efficiency.

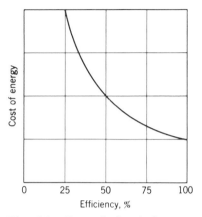

Fig. 6.2 Cost of electrical energy versus motor efficiency.

depend on cost and the quality of performance is otherwise satisfactory. In Fig. 6.1, the cost of the electric motor is shown as a function of the efficiency. In Fig. 6.2, the cost of energy for the period equal to the life of the motor is shown as a function of efficiency. Figure 6.3 shows the combined cost of motor and energy as a function of efficiency. For very low values of efficiency, the cost is high, since the consumption and consequent cost of energy are very high. At high values of efficiency, the cost again is high, since the motor itself is very expensive. At an intermediate point there is a total cost that is less than any other. Selection of a motor with an efficiency corresponding to this minimum point would be dictated by the criterion of optimizing the total cost.

If the noise level of the electric motor must be considered, optimization requires an additional criterion. It has been found that the more expensive motors are quieter, as would be reasonable. Without consideration of noise level, it was relatively simple to make a decision concerning total cost. The cost of the energy and the cost of the motor were clearly defined and could be added directly. If it is possible to put a dollar value on the noise level, then the cost associated with noise level can be added to the cost of energy and the cost of the motor.

The possibility of optimizing with respect to two criteria must be considered. In this connection, it is frequently stated that it would be desirable to attain "the production of the greatest good for the greatest number." This could be reworded, in the case of the electric motor, thus: "Design to obtain the quietest, cheapest combination of electric motor and energy cost." This is impossible, as can be shown by reviewing the electric-motor problem.

The electric motor with the lowest combined cost of motor and energy is one in the middle range. The more expensive motors are quieter; hence a motor giving the cheapest combination of motor and energy is not the quietest. If we take the quietest motor, we have a very expensive motor-energy combination.

Now, if we place a value on the noise level, as indicated in Fig. 6.4, which shows a decreasing cost assignable to noise level with increasing efficiency, we can add this cost directly to the cost of the motor and the cost of electrical energy and find a total cost, indicated in Fig. 6.5. This assignment of a cost might be arbitrary or based on studies of the effects of noise on the environment. The addition of this factor moves the minimum-cost point toward the higher efficiencies, and the selection of a motor with a higher efficiency would be dictated. However, we cannot now say that we have selected the cheapest, quietest electric motor. We have selected an electric motor that gives an optimum performance when the cost of energy, the cost of the motor, and the cost of noise are considered. If the cost assigned to noise is increased, the minimum-total point moves

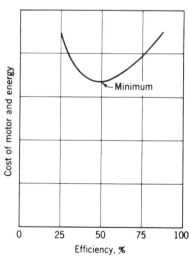

Fig. 6.3 Cost of motor and energy versus efficiency.

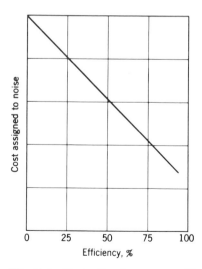

Fig. 6.4 Cost of noise versus efficiency.

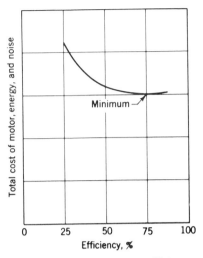

Fig. 6.5   Total cost versus efficiency.

toward the higher efficiencies, and conversely if the cost of noise is decreased.

In this chapter we shall consider, very briefly, certain methods available for use in the optimization of systems and components. The mathematics associated with optimization has progressed rapidly in the past several years, and much of it is beyond the present discussion. The need for certain of these advanced methods will be indicated in the ensuing discussions.

6.2.   Elementary Optimization Problems

We shall consider the problem of enclosing a rectangular area of a plane surface by a fence, illustrated in Fig. 6.6. The field has the length L and the width W. It is proposed to fence a specified area with the minimum amount of fencing. If the ratio between L and

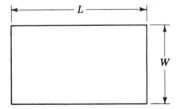

Fig. 6.6   Fencing of field.

W is subject to selection, the shape of the rectangle that has the maximum area for a given length of fence or, conversely, a minimum length of fence for a given area can be found. To facilitate the analysis, let the ratio between width and length be represented by the variable x; thus,

$$x = \frac{W}{L}$$

It follows then that the area A is

$$A = WL = xL^2$$
$$\text{or} \quad L = \sqrt{\frac{A}{x}}$$

The total length of fence T is

$$T = 2(W + L)$$
$$\text{or} \quad T = 2(xL + L) = 2L(1 + x)$$

Substituting for L gives

$$T = 2\sqrt{\frac{A}{x}}\,(1 + x)$$

which can be written as

$$T = 2\sqrt{A}\left(\frac{1}{\sqrt{x}} + \sqrt{x}\right)$$

The quantity $T/2\sqrt{A}$ is plotted as a function of x in Fig. 6.7. At $x = 1$, it is a minimum. Since A is a constant, T is a minimum at the same time that $T/2\sqrt{A}$ is a minimum. This optimum value of x can readily be found by the methods of the calculus, as shown below.

The optimum length of fence, T, is found by taking the derivative with respect to x and equating it to zero; thus,

$$\frac{dT}{dx} = 2\sqrt{A}\left(-\frac{1}{2}\frac{1}{x^{3/2}} + \frac{1}{2}\frac{1}{\sqrt{x}}\right) = 0$$

Solving for x,

$$-\frac{1}{x^{3/2}} + \frac{1}{\sqrt{x}} = 0 \qquad \text{or} \qquad x = 1$$

With $x = 1$, the most efficient shape to minimize the cost of fencing for a rectangular field of given area is the square, thus providing four sides of equal length and a minimum length of fence for the given area.   Conversely, a given length of fence will enclose the maximum rectangular area when the rectangle is a square.

This elementary procedure is satisfactory if the problems are completely deterministic; in other words, the facts can be expressed in the form of algebraic equations and then elementary operations of the calculus used to maximize or minimize the dependent variable.

A problem which is introductory to interesting and important missile problems of great complexity can be solved by the methods discussed earlier.   In Fig. 6.8 a projectile has been fired with an

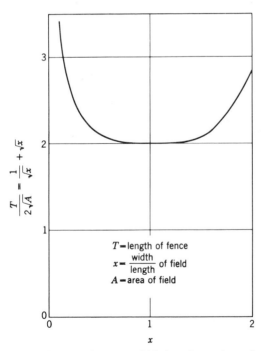

Fig. 6.7 Optimum width-length ratio of fenced area.

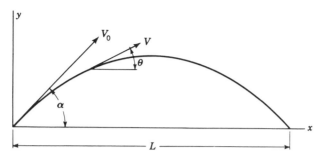

Fig. 6.8 Projectile trajectory.

initial velocity of V_0, at an angle α with the horizontal. It is assumed that there is no air resistance and that the only force acting upon the projectile is the constant gravitational attraction which exerts a downward force mg, acting on the projectile at all times.

When artillery first came into being, one of the major problems was to determine the angle α that would yield the greatest range. A solution of this problem that gives a crude first approximation to the angle is reasonably satisfactory for very small velocities but is not realistic for projectile velocities near the velocity of sound. This solution is obtained as follows:

The initial velocity of the projectile is V_0 at an angle α with the horizontal. The velocity at any time is V at an angle θ with the horizontal.

The vertical or y component of the velocity at any time is

$$V_y = V \sin \theta \tag{6.1}$$

The horizontal or x component is

$$V_x = V \cos \theta \tag{6.2}$$

The only force acting on the projectile is the gravitational force mg since friction is neglected, giving an acceleration g vertically downward. The horizontal velocity is therefore constant and given by

$$V_x = V_0 \cos \alpha \tag{6.3}$$

The vertical velocity is, at any time,

$$V_y = V_0 \sin \alpha - gt \tag{6.4}$$

The horizontal distance x from the origin to the location of the projectile at any time is found by the use of Eq. (6.3) for V_x as follows:

With constant velocity V_x in the x direction, starting from $x = 0$ at $t = 0$, the distance traveled is

$$x = V_0 t \cos \alpha \tag{6.5}$$

In the vertical direction the acceleration is constant, the initial velocity is V_0, and the initial displacement at $t = 0$ is zero. The displacement y is, then,

$$y = V_0 t \sin \alpha - \frac{gt^2}{2} \tag{6.6}$$

The time required for the projectile to travel to its destination at distance L horizontally from the origin is found by solving Eq. (6.6) for t; thus,

at $\quad x = L \qquad y = 0$

then $\quad 0 = V_0 t \sin \alpha - \dfrac{gt^2}{2}$

or $\quad t^2 - \dfrac{2V_0}{g} t \sin \alpha = 0$

and $\quad t - \dfrac{2V_0}{g} \sin \alpha = 0$

Hence, $\quad t = \dfrac{2V_0}{g} \sin \alpha \tag{6.7}$

Substitution for t in the expression (6.5) for x yields

$$x = V_0 \cos \alpha \, \frac{2V_0}{g} \sin \alpha$$

or $\quad L = x = \dfrac{V_0^2}{g} \sin 2\alpha \tag{6.8}$

The maximum range L is obtained when $\sin 2\alpha$ is maximum. This occurs when $2\alpha = 90°$ or $\alpha = 45°$ and $\sin 2\alpha = 1$. Substitution for $\sin \alpha$ yields the maximum range in a frictionless case as

$$L_{\max} = \frac{V_0^2}{g} \tag{6.9}$$

This simple trajectory problem has very little direct practical application; moreover, the solution of the real problem is much more complex. The maximum range that can be attained with a very-high-velocity projectile is influenced by the air resistance and the curvature of the earth, as well as the variation of the gravitational constant with distance from the earth's center. If all these factors are taken into consideration, the resulting equation, a differential equation, is far too difficult to solve with any methods within the scope of this discussion. However, the problem lends itself well to solution by means of the digital computer. This, in fact, is the method used in all modern work on satellite orbits and projectile or missile paths.

6.3.   Value Judgments

We now consider other problems in optimization that do not lend themselves to elementary solutions or to rigorous and single-valued solutions, even with all available modern methods for the solution of the mathematical problems that arise. We shall also discuss some of the more difficult problems and the available methods for solution, even though these methods may be beyond the scope of our present treatment of problems. We shall develop the concepts involved and outline the procedures that are followed in these cases.

The general problem of optimization of a design is to maximize performance with respect to a criterion. For example, in a single component, such as an electric motor, the ratio between power output and power input, the efficiency, is the performance characteristic that is frequently maximized. In the earlier examples relative to fencing a plane area and obtaining the maximum range of a projectile, relatively elementary conditions obtained. In the case of fencing an area, we wish to maximize the area with respect to the length of fence. In the case of the projectile, the range is maximized with respect to the energy available. These are very straightforward problems, where the selection of a criterion does not present any real difficulty.

However, there are problems in which it becomes difficult to define the criterion with respect to which optimization is to be achieved. For example, let us consider a manufactured product which weighs w pounds and costs c dollars. Let us assume that this product is made in several different styles and qualities. The heavier models are the cheaper ones, and the light-weight models are more expensive. We shall assume that insofar as quality is concerned, that is, life, cost of

Table 6.1

Product	Weight, lb	Price
1	1	$10
2	2	7
3	4	5
4	8	3
5	10	2

maintenance, safety, and the like, they are all equally satisfactory. The purchaser, however, must decide whether he wants a heavy, cheap model or an expensive, light-weight model. In order to make a decision, some value must be placed on the weight of the object. If the product simply stands in one place and is not moved about, then its weight is of no great concern to the purchaser, and he would be likely to buy the cheapest one available. On the other hand, if it is a household appliance which the housewife uses and finds distasteful if too heavy to move, there would be an inclination to place a considerable value on the lighter weight. However, in order to make a meaningful decision, one must find some way of evaluating this quality described as light weight.

The customer desires to maximize his satisfaction from the use of his purchase. His satisfaction cannot be described simply in terms of the dollar price paid. Let us suppose that the product is available in the sizes and at the prices indicated in Table 6.1. Let us now suppose that a prospective purchaser makes a value judgment and decides that the lightest product, the 1-lb one, is worth 10 units to him; that the second one, weighing 2 lb, would be worth only 8; the third, 6; the fourth, 4; and the fifth, 2. These are possible realistic evaluations on the basis of an estimate of the value of the light-weight product. Let us now divide the value, as judged by the purchaser, by the price he has to pay. Product 1 would be 1 unit of value per dollar, product 2, 1.14, etc., as shown below:

Product	*Units of value*
1	1.0
2	1.14
3	1.2
4	1.3
5	1.0

Consider another purchaser, making a somewhat different evaluation. He decides that the heaviest object is worth just 1 unit of value, etc.

Weight, lb	Units of value
10	1
8	2
4	4
2	8
1	16

In other words, he places sixteen times the value on the light-weight one that he does on the heavy one. Once again, dividing the value as judged by the purchaser by the price, a series of numbers results: 1.6, 1.14, 0.8, 0.67, and 0.5. Two different customers, making different value judgments, arrive at different optimum purchases, from their standpoint. The first customer would buy the 8-lb product, at a cost of 1.3 units of value per dollar of purchase price. The second purchaser would take the lightest-weight product, getting 1.6 units of value per dollar. The manufacturer, in turn, must estimate the value judgments that will be made by prospective customers and then make a decision concerning the line of products he will produce in order to maximize the profit in the business.

When the evaluation of an output, a product, or a process cannot be based on a single obvious criterion, e.g., cost or efficiency, value judgments must be made. Assignments of values to establish acceptable criteria may be quite arbitrary. The example cited above illustrates this point. Practical applications of this procedure will now be discussed.

During the past half century, the development of systems designed to utilize the waters of a large river has demanded the creation of a scale to evaluate the feasibility of such projects. Generally, these river-system projects include the building of a dam or series of dams, the generation of power at these dams, the regulation of flood water, the supplying of irrigation waters, and the development of recreation areas. The costs of such a development include the acquisition of the land; the construction of the dams, irrigation canals, and flood-control works; the purchase of equipment for power and water distribution systems; and all the physical features. In the design of the system, it is necessary to maximize the benefits in some reasonable manner or to minimize the cost per unit of benefit. If the problem involved only the construction of a dam for the generation of power, one could, with relative ease, justify the project or not, as the case might be, on the basis of the design that minimized the cost of the power generated or that maximized the net income from the sale of power. No such simple procedure is possible in the case of a multipurpose river-development system, which is necessary since a single-purpose design will seldom pay off in terms of income exceeding cost.

The feasibility of a multipurpose river system is decided on the basis of the magnitude of the ratio of benefits to cost. This ratio is established in the following manner:

An estimate of total cost is made; this is really the easiest part of the problem. Although the cost of land acquisition is subject to increase when a development is announced, a figure for the cost of the land can be established. A reasonable estimate of the construction costs and of the cost of equipment can be made. The sum of all costs fixes the capital investment that is needed. The annual cost is computed on the basis of the cost of the capital investment in terms of depreciation and interest payments and the cost of operation of the system in terms of repair, maintenance, and the like.

On the income side, the probable income from the generated power and the sale of irrigation waters can be estimated; however, placing a value on flood control and recreational facilities is less easily accomplished. Each of these provides benefits that would be acknowledged by any reasonable person, but it is extremely difficult to place a numerical value on them. In spite of this, estimates of use of recreational facilities provide numerical values that are used to fix an annual benefit in dollars derived from these facilities. The savings likely to be effected from the reduction in flood damage are estimated and reduced to an average annual figure. Any other benefits are treated in a similar manner, and finally a dollar value is assigned for the total annual income to be expected from the river-development system.

The final figure of merit is obtained by dividing the sum of the annual benefits by the sum of annual maintenance, operation, and capital costs. If the ratio is equal to or exceeds 1, the project is deemed feasible if other factors, notably political ones, justify its construction. It is easy to see, from this example, that in any system design involving outputs affecting human beings, on which it is difficult to place either a dollar or other commonly accepted value, great difficulty is encountered in optimizing the design or even justifying the project itself. The Tennessee Valley development was and is controversial primarily because of differences of opinion on the value of benefits and the amount of the real costs.

Even if one is able to place reasonable values on the outputs of a system, the problem of optimization itself is often difficult. This encouraged development of techniques and tools to aid in the optimization procedure. We shall describe briefly two of these.

6.4. Linear Programming and Game Theory

We have indicated above that in many problems in system design it is desirable to be able to optimize performance with respect to accepted criteria, but solutions are beyond the scope of the elementary mathematical procedures used earlier. Other tools are available, and two of these will now be discussed: linear programming and game theory.

Linear programming is a technique of mathematical modeling that is applicable to a particular class of problems and can lead to optimization with respect to prescribed criteria. The models are characterized by two kinds of linear equations. First, a linear equation expresses the relationship between an appropriate quantity, such as cost, and the parameters of the system. Secondly, a set of linear equations expresses the constraints on the operation.

For example, the cost of a product might be expressed by the equation

$$C = Ax_1 + Bx_2$$

where C is the cost of the product and A and B are the unit costs of components used in the quantities x_1 and x_2, respectively.

A set of equations of the following form could represent the constraints on the process that must be considered.

$$a_1x_1 + b_1x_2 \geqq p_1 \tag{6.10}$$
$$a_2x_1 + b_2x_2 \geqq p_2 \tag{6.11}$$
$$a_3x_1 + b_3x_2 \geqq p_3 \tag{6.12}$$

The cost C is to be minimized within the constraints imposed by Eqs. (6.10) to (6.12).

One can visualize C as a function of the two coordinates x_1 and x_2 which can be represented by a surface in the C, x_1, x_2 coordinate system. This surface would be a plane surface sloping upward from the $x_1 x_2$ plane, with the slope fixed by the coefficients A and B. We stipulate that x_1 and x_2 be equal to or greater than zero, thus limiting the region of applicability.

The equations for p_1, p_2, and p_3 define lines in the $x_1 x_2$ plane, and these in turn define a polygon. The region on one side of the boundary of the polygon represents feasible operation; on the other side, it is not feasible. Lines of equal cost in the plane $C = f(x_1, x_2)$ are parallel to the $x_1 x_2$ plane. The vertex of the polygon in the $x_1 x_2$ plane that, when projected upward to the C plane, gives the minimum C is the point that defines operation at minimum possible cost.

If the equations describing the system or process are linear but involve more than two independent variables, such as x_1 and x_2, it is essentially impossible to visualize the meaning of the equations in terms of a geometrical space problem. However, it is possible to solve such problems by techniques which have been developed extensively in recent years. Notable among these is the simplex method,[1] which provides a systematic procedure for solving any number of linear equations and obtaining a minimal solution.

The application of the technique of linear programming in a very elementary case encompasses the manufacture of products X and Y in a factory using three distinct processes, A, B, and C, in the production of each. The maximum number of items that can be put through each process per day is shown in Table 6.2. The profit on product X is 50 per cent more than on product Y. It is desired that the profit of the total operation be maximized by processing the appropriate number of each product to ensure this maximum.

The capacity of process A is either 3,000 X's or 1,300 Y's; this fact can be incorporated in a mathematical statement of the form

$$x + 2.31y = 3,000$$

[1] O. B. Dantzig, Formulating and Solving Linear Programs, in E. F. Beckenbach (ed.), "Modern Mathematics for the Engineer," 2d ser., pp. 213–227, McGraw-Hill Book Company, New York, 1961.

Table 6.2

Process	Product	
	X	Y
A	3,000	1,300
B	1,000	2,000
C	1,200	1,500

where x and y indicate, respectively, the number of units of X and Y processed per day. The correctness of this statement is clear if we note that the time required to process a Y item is $1/1,300$ of a day and to process an X item is $1/3,000$ of a day, and the time required to process x items is $x/3,000$ and y items is $y/1,300$. The total time T required to process $x + y$ items is

$$T = \frac{x}{3,000} + \frac{y}{1,300}$$

Multiplying by 3,000,

$$3,000T = x + 2.31y$$

and letting $T = 1$ day, we have, finally,

$$3,000 = x + 2.31y$$

Similarly, for the processes B and C, we obtain

$$2x + y = 2,000$$
$$1.25x + y = 1,500$$

The profit P per day is given by

$$P = 1.5x + y$$

where the profit per item Y is unity.

Consider, now, that there is only one process involved, process A. We can compute the profits from this process alone, using the profit equation and substituting for the value of x that given by the equation for process A. We have then, from process A,

$$x = 3,000 - 2.31y$$

but $$P = 1.5(3,000 - 2.31y) + y$$

Hence, $$P = 4,500 - 3.46y + y$$

and finally, $$P = 4,500 - 2.46y \qquad (6.13)$$

This shows that the profit will be greatest when none of product Y is made. This straightforward result requires no very sophisticated analysis. However, when we bring into the consideration the facts concerning processes B and C, the result is not quite so obvious. We continue, therefore, with the analysis to determine the best operation to maximize profits.

It is required that values of the numbers of units x and y be established to make P a maximum within the constraints placed by the processing times. In Fig. 6.9 the equations for processes A and B are shown in graphical form. The lines A and B intersect at $x = 447.5$ and $y = 1,105$. These numbers of items can be handled in the processing sequence A, B. All other combinations represented by points in the shaded area can be processed. Points to the right of and above the boundaries of the shaded area are not feasible. Only points lying between a line and the origin are possible.

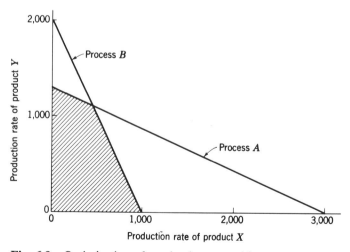

Fig. 6.9 Optimization of production rate with two processes.

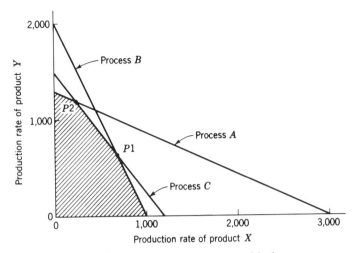

Fig. 6.10 Optimization of production rate with three processes.

To examine the validity of the last statement, consider a point to the right of and above the line *A*; for example, $x = 1,000$, $y = 1,500$. The times in process A are: for *x*, 1 day/3,000, and for *y*, 1 day/1,300. The total time T_T with this combination is

$$T_T = 1,000 \frac{1}{3,000} + \frac{1,500}{1,300} = 0.33 + 1.15 = 1.48 \text{ days}$$

This is clearly outside the realm of possibility with the installed equipment, and it can be shown that this is so for all points to the right of and above the boundaries of the shaded area.

In Fig. 6.10, the line for process C has been added, and the final shaded area is defined as the area between the lines and the origin common to all the lines. The two vertices bounding this area have the coordinates

	x	y
P1	666.7	666.7
P2	250	1,190

The profits associated with these points are

Point	Profit
$P1: P = 1.5 \times 666.7 + 666.7$	$= 1,666.7$
$P2: P = 1.5 \times 250 + 1,190$	$= 1,565$

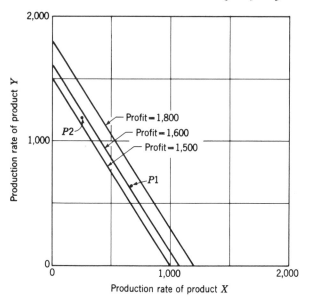

Fig. 6.11   Profit as a function of production.

That point $P1$ is the more profitable can be demonstrated in a different manner by considering lines of equal profit shown in Fig. 6.11.   These lines have a y intercept equal to the profit and an x intercept equal to two-thirds of the profit; thus,

$$P = 1.5x + y$$
If $x = 0$ $y = P$
If $y = 0$ $x = \dfrac{P}{1.5}$

These lines of equal profit show increasing profit as the distance from the origin increases.   The distance measured perpendicularly from $P1$ to a line through the origin parallel to the equal-profit lines is greater than that from $P2$ to the same line.   It was noted earlier that the maximum production possible is 1,000 X's and 1,300 Y's. However, this lies far outside the shaded area of Fig. 6.9 and is therefore not possible of attainment with the present equipment.

In conclusion, the most profitable operation is represented by point $P1$, with an equal number of x and y, and yields a profit of 1,667 times the profit on one item Y.   This method is applicable to similar situations in which various methods of operation are possible and it is not obvious which of them is optimum.

In circumstances involving a competitive aspect, notably in military affairs, business, and the like, the theory of games or, as sometimes called, the theory of games and strategy, is an important tool. The objective of this theory is to find an optimum strategy that gives the player of the game the greatest expected value of payoff. This theory is an accepted aspect of mathematical theory. In the case of very simple games, such as checkers or Nim, it is possible to work out a complete strategy to ensure that the player maximizes his gain. In the practical situations of daily life, the conflict can seldom be reduced to the terms of a simple game, the strategy of which can be delineated by mathematical procedures. However, the methods described in the theory of games and strategy may shed light on the total problem and assist in obtaining a workable solution.

Let us consider a game in which two players, A and B, participate. This game, in which, if one person wins, the other loses exactly the same amount, is called the two-person zero-sum game. It represents a very large class of games, for aggregations of people can be considered as one person, and the game is two-person if there are two adversaries, regardless of their actual makeup in terms of number of people.

Certain terminology of game theory is introduced at this time[1] to facilitate reference to more extensive discussions of the topic.

> If the game is one in which both players have complete knowledge of the present situation and past moves, it is called one of perfect information. Checkers and chess are in this class; poker is not.
>
> A move is a point in the play at which a player has a set of alternatives, and his choice is the alternative he selects.
>
> A play is a complete set of moves by both players.
>
> After the play, there is a payoff.
>
> Rules define legal moves and method of payoff.
>
> Strategy is a complete plan for moves throughout the play.

Suppose that in a game each player has two courses of action open to him. We shall denote these as $A1$ and $A2$ and $B1$ and $B2$, respectively. Let us now stipulate that the profit to A in the case of

---

[1] H. H. Goode and R. E. Machol, "System Engineering," pp. 358–359, McGraw-Hill Book Company, New York, 1957.

Table 6.3

	$B1$	$B2$	Row minima
$A1$	$+1$	-1	-1
$A2$	-1	$+1$	-1
Column maxima	$+1$	$+1$	

each of the four possible actions will be as shown in Table 6.3. If player A takes action 1 and player B takes action 1, player A profits by 1 unit, whereas, had player A taken action 1 and player B action 2, player A would have lost 1 unit.

The employment of a matrix in this manner to describe the play of a game is useful and will be illustrated in the following descriptions. However, before proceeding, it is well to define two features of the matrix. Referring again to Table 6.3, we see two terms listed, namely, column maxima and row minima. Each of these is simply the value of the payoff that is the maximum in the column or the minimum in the row.

Refer, now, to Table 6.4, which describes a different game. In this case, the payoff to player A is always positive. In other words, no matter what he does or what player B does, player A will win some amount. However, it is also apparent that, under some circumstances, player A will win a great deal more than he would under other circumstances. This, of course, would be known to both players. It would therefore be prudent for each of them to devise a strategy that would provide the best results for each, respectively. Let us consider the strategy of player A. He notes that, if player B selects strategy 1, player A can ensure winning 4 units if he selects strategy 2. However, if player B selects strategy 2, player

Table 6.4

	$B1$	$B2$	Row minima
$A1$	1	2	1
$A2$	4	③	3
Column maxima	4	3	

A is limited to a maximum win of 3 units.   It is immediately apparent
that player A should select strategy 2, since this will make certain
that his winnings are greater than if he selected strategy 1.   Player B,
looking at the same situation, would note that, if he selected strategy
1, he would be in danger of losing 4 units, whereas if he selected
strategy 2 his maximum loss would be only 3 units.   Accordingly,
player B would select strategy 2 to minimize his losses.   Both players
therefore decide that strategy 2 is better; in the resulting play, each of
the players will use strategy 2 with a gain of 3 for A and a loss of 3
for B.   We note that the minimum value of the column maxima is
equal to the maximum value of the row minima, namely, the value 3.
In such cases we say that there is a saddle point, which is marked in
Table 6.4 by a circle around the number 3.

Table 6.5 shows a third game in which the minimum value of
the column maxima does not coincide with the maximum value of the
row minima.   In fact, these two values are $+2$ and -2, respectively.
This produces a quite different result if two intelligent players are
engaged in the game.   Each would have the matrix available and,
from A's standpoint, he would wish to play strategy 1, since his
maximum gain could be as great as 3 and his maximum loss -1.   If
player B were to choose strategy 1, his best gain would be 1 and he
might suffer a loss of 2.   On the other hand, if he chooses strategy 2,
he might lose as much as 3 and gain as much as 2.   If he looks at it
from the standpoint of minimizing his possible losses, it would appear
that player A would select strategy 1, and player B strategy 1.   This
would result in a loss of 1 for A and a gain of 1 for B.   However,
under these circumstances, A would realize that B would select
strategy 1, and A would then be inclined to select strategy 2, since
he would effect a profit of 2.   Then B would realize what A was
doing and would therefore select strategy 2, by which he would gain

Table 6.5

	B1	B2	Row minima
A1	-1	$+3$	-1
A2	$+2$	-2	-2
Column maxima	$+2$	$+3$	

2. The situation is, quite clearly, unstable as compared with that shown in Table 6.4.

A review of the situation depicted in Table 6.4 clarifies this point. Player A notes that with strategy 2, no matter what strategy B plays, he will be better off than if he plays strategy 1. Likewise, B notes that, if he plays strategy 2, his maximum loss is 3, whereas if he were to play strategy 1, he could lose as much as 4. Consequently, in this case it is better for each player to play strategy 2. The concept of minimizing one's possible losses determines this manner of play; in the case of the game in Table 6.5, minimizing one's maximum possible losses does not result in the same situation. Only in the case of a game in which there is a saddle point is it possible to have a pure strategy that will be followed by each player and that will result in a stable game.

However, in the game shown in Table 6.5, each of the players can devise a strategy that will result in the best game. They use what is termed a mixed strategy. If the game continues over a period of time, each player uses a different play on successive moves. He determines a frequency that he should use for each play. For example, in the game of Table 6.5, player A might decide to use strategy 1 half the time and strategy 2 half the time. Likewise, player B might decide to use strategy 1 one-third of the time and strategy 2 two-thirds of the time. In any case, each player could determine a sequence of play that would result in a calculable reward to each of them.

Let us consider now what the result of the game will be if player A determines to play strategy 1 with a frequency of n and strategy 2 with a frequency of $1 - n$. Likewise, player B will play strategy 1 with a frequency of m and strategy 2 with a frequency of $1 - m$. Under these circumstances, we can calculate the payoff to each of the players. The payoff to player A is shown in the Table 6.6. We

Table 6.6

	Frequency	$B1$ m	$B2$ $1 - m$
$A1$	n	-1	$+3$
$A2$	$1 - n$	$+2$	-2

shall calculate the payoff, using the proposed strategy. In the matrix, the combination $A1$, $B1$ has a payoff of -1 to player A, and we note that this will be played with a frequency of n by player A and with a frequency of m by player B. Consequently, the product $mn(-1)$ is the expected payoff to player A from this portion of the matrix. Likewise, for the strategy $A2$, $B1$, we have $(+2)m(1-n)$ as the payoff from this portion of the matrix to player A. For $A1$, $B2$, we have $(+3)n(1-m)$, and for the portion $A2$, $B2$, we have $(-2)(1-n)(1-m)$. The sum of all these is the expected payoff E to player A, which is given by

$$E = 4m - 8mn + 5n - 2$$

Each player has control over this payoff in his selection of the ratio m or n, as the case may be.

We shall now investigate the effect of variation in the value of m and n. If we differentiate the expression for E with respect to m, we find the rate at which E changes as m is varied, which is written

$$\frac{\partial E}{\partial m} = 4 - 8n$$

We now equate this to zero to obtain the maximum value of E and solve for n; we find that $n = \frac{1}{2}$. Similarly, in the case of differentiation with respect to n, we have

$$\frac{\partial E}{\partial n} = -8m + 5 = 0$$

or $m = \frac{5}{8}$

Substitution of these values in the expression for E shows that $E = \frac{1}{2}$ in each case. To determine graphically the significance of these findings, we plot, in Fig. 6.12, the expected return from B's viewpoint in terms of his variation of strategy and A's playing either pure strategy 1 or pure strategy 2. When A plays pure strategy 1, then $n = 1$, and the expected payoff to B is

$$-E = 4m - 3$$

The line called $A1$, in Fig. 6.12, shows this equation graphically.

Similarly, the line $A2$ expresses the payoff

$$-E = 2 - 4m$$

when A uses strategy 2. These lines intersect at a value of $m = 0.625$, where $E = \frac{1}{2}$. This indicates that, no matter what startegy A may use, B can make certain of losing no more than $\frac{1}{2}$, provided he plays strategy 1 62.5 per cent of the time. Likewise, in Fig. 6.13, from A's viewpoint, expected payoffs to A in terms of B playing pure strategy 2 are plotted. These two lines intersect at the point $n = \frac{1}{2}$ and show an expected payoff of $\frac{1}{2}$ to A. Therefore, if A plays each strategy one-half of the time, he can do no worse than win $\frac{1}{2}$ unit. We find, then, that this game can be played by each player with a strategy that will maximize his return and guarantee that, no matter what the other player does, he will be certain of the best possible return.

The corollary to this analysis, in which it is assumed that each player is intelligent and fully conversant with the facts and the methods to be used by the other, is that, if a player should discover that his opponent was not using the optimum strategy, for example, in the case of the game analyzed above, if B should discover that A was using strategy 1 all the time, his wise move would be to use

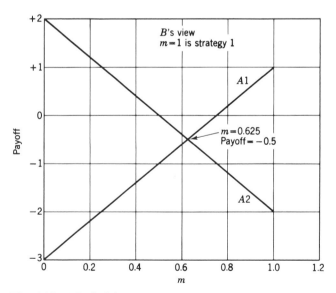

Fig. 6.12 Maximizing payoff in two-person game.

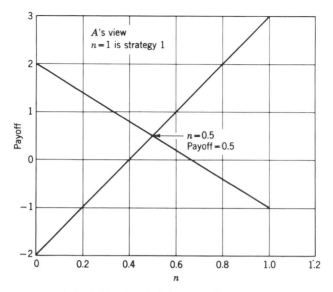

Fig. 6.13 Maximizing payoff in two-player game.

strategy 1 all the time himself.   Under these circumstances, he would increase his payoff to $+1$, contrasted with the $-\frac{1}{2}$ which would be a result of his opponent's playing strategy 1 one-half of the time and strategy 2 the other half of the time.

This game is extremely elementary and is unlikely to be the exact counterpart of a real situation.   However, it illustrates the elementary concepts of game theory, and one can extend these to more complex circumstances, using more sophisticated methods of analysis.

Problems

6.1.   A cylindrical tank with a capacity of 1,000 cu ft costs $10 per square foot for the cylindrical walls and $12 per square foot for the circular ends.   What is the best diameter to minimize the cost?   What is the best diameter if the cylindrical walls cost $10 per square foot and the circular ends cost $20 per square foot?

6.2.   A factory manufactures two products, x and y.   Each product goes through three processes: machining, assembling, and painting.   Product x sells for $17 each, and product y for

$16. The cost of operating the processes are: machining, $250 per hour; assembling, $600 per hour; painting, $700 per hour. The number of units per day that can be processed for each of the products is shown in the tabulation below.

Process	x	y
Machining	1,600	800
Assembling	1,000	1,000
Painting	800	1,600

Plan the operation for the most profit in an 8-hr day.

6.3. Optimize the traffic flow of Prob. 5.4, with congestion in both directions, with two lanes east and west and four lanes north and south. Establish a suitable criterion.

References

Asimow, Morris: "Introduction to Design," pp. 84–121, Prentice-Hall, Inc., Englewood Cliffs, N.J., 1962.

Goode, H. H., and R. E. Machol: "System Engineering," pp. 334–343, 357–377, 379–388, McGraw-Hill Book Company, New York, 1957.

Parzen, Emanuel: "Modern Probability Theory and Its Applications," John Wiley & Sons, Inc., New York, 1960.

Feedback Control

7.1. General Principles The technology of the twentieth century has spawned a controversial and revolutionary labor-saving technique, automation. Realization that automatic machinery is replacing people in many operations that are an integral part of current-day technology causes anxiety. Automatic machinery has been in existence for a very long time; however, the automatic machinery of the mid-twentieth century differs from that of the nineteenth to an important degree because of feedback control.

Fully automatic machines turning out products of varying degrees of complexity were in common use at the beginning of the twentieth century. Their inability to control the quality of their product automatically was a critical weakness. For example, a machine which formed and threaded bolts might progressively turn out threads that deviated erratically and continuously to a greater degree from the desired form. When this deviation from the ideal became objectionable, the human operator took over control to correct the error. If the operator were not alert to the situation, the resultant production of inadequate substandard items might continue over a considerable period of time. This hastened the use of feedback control to provide the continuous monitoring of a process that is the essence of automation.

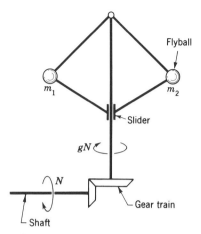

Fig. 7.1   Flyball governor.

An example of a very old feedback control mechanism is the flyball governor, which can provide control of the speed of rotation of a shaft powered by a steam engine.   Steam engines used to drive steamships, generators, or other mechanical devices require control to operate at a constant speed.   A rather obvious way to attain this end is to incorporate a human operator in the system.   He observes the speed of rotation of the shaft and, when it deviates from the desired speed, makes an adjustment in the input to the steam engine. In this manner the speed can be controlled within the limitations of the human operator.

The operator observes the output speed N, compares this with the desired speed N_o, notes the difference in the two, and makes a correction, that is, an increase or a decrease in the input to the steam engine, to increase or decrease N, depending upon the sign of the quantity $N_o - N$.   If N_o is larger than N, he increases N.   If N is larger than N_o, a negative value of the difference $N_o - N$, he will decrease N.

If, for the human operator in this process, we substitute the flyball governor, truly automatic control is attained.   The flyball governor operates on the basis of the physical fact that, as speed of rotation increases, a mass attached to the rotating shaft exerts a greater force on the connecting link between shaft and mass.   The flyball governor itself is illustrated in Fig. 7.1.   As speed increases, the masses m_1 and m_2 tend to move upward and outward.   This results in a motion of the sleeve *S*. If this is connected to a valve that controls the rate at which steam is admitted to the engine, so that, as the sleeve *S* moves upward, the rate of flow of steam is decreased, we have feedback which introduces a correction to reduce the error in the output. This is called negative feedback. A detailed analysis of feedback control will be undertaken following the introduction of background material.

It has been noted that automatic control of systems is not new. One of the earliest examples of an automatically controlled operation was that of the old-style player piano, operated from a tape punched much as modern computer tape is punched. It was a very much larger piece of tape, and it actuated not an electronic apparatus but rather a simple mechanical tool. The automatic loom was used in textile mills about a hundred years ago. It was operated by punched cards in a manner similar to that of the modern-day computer. However, these were not fully automatic systems since they lacked that one vital characteristic of the automatic control system: feedback. If an error occurred, the machine did not sense it and proceeded with its action even though the product might be totally useless.

To illustrate use of feedback in a situation familiar in daily life, Fig. 7.2 is a block diagram describing the control of automobile speed by a human operator. He decides upon a speed appropriate for the highway on which he is driving. This is the reference speed. He observes the actual speed by looking at the speedometer. He makes a mental note of the relationship between observed speed and desired speed. If he is traveling too slowly, he depresses the accelerator in proportion to the deficiency in speed. This action supplies more fuel to the engine and the car speeds up. If a later observation

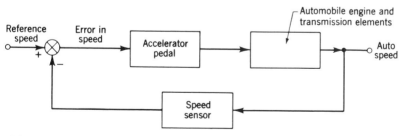

Fig. 7.2 Block diagram of simple feedback system: automobile speed control.

reveals a speed higher than desired, the driver releases his pressure on the accelerator and the car slows down.

This entire operation can be performed by mechanical, electrical, or hydraulic means. For the visual observation of the speedometer one can substitute an electric generator producing a voltage proportional to speed. The voltage can be compared with a reference voltage which in turn is proportional to the desired speed. The difference is the error signal which, when fed to a solenoid, positions the throttle to increase or decrease speed, as may be appropriate.

If one considers the possibility of automatic control of automobile speed without the use of feedback, he sees immediately the difficulties encountered in such control of any process. If one wishes to program automobile speed on an expressway, the grade and curvature of which are known throughout its length, he can argue that a setting of the throttle that would be adjusted in accordance with highway grade is a means to this end. True, it would be possible to program in advance the necessary throttle setting to give a desired speed on any highway that can be described in terms of a coordinate giving distance from the starting point and surface slope at that point. However, wind resistance is a parameter that cannot be predicted in advance. If there were no natural wind, it could be done, since the relationship between air resistance and speed is reasonably well established. A natural tail or head wind would, however, destroy the program completely. Wind in this case is analogous to noise in an electrical or electronic system. An unpredictable outside disturbance will destroy the performance if the program makes no allowance for such disturbance.

Feedback eliminates, to a major degree, the deterioration of performance caused by outside disturbance. The driver of a car compensates for road grade, wind, and traffic alike in his role of speed sensor, error measurer, and error corrector.

As a very rough guide to an appreciation of the economic role of feedback, it is sometimes stated that cost of control with feedback is approximately one-tenth of that of a comparable quality control without it. Certainly in the case of automobile speed control, such would be the case. In fact, it is doubtful that any other method would be feasible at all in this situation.

It is pertinent to note here that the automatic loom required the highest degree of precision in its construction to produce the desired output.   If the work were to be of the expected quality, no deviations of any significant magnitude from the ideal could be tolerated.   To the uninitiated, it might seem that improving upon the automatic loom would require producing one to perform with even greater precision.   The control by feedback eliminates this necessity.   No better performance is required at any stage of the operation than in the case of the old loom; rather, a continuous measurement of the output is made and compared with the expected output and suitable corrections are made.   This is a most important characteristic of an automatic system with feedback and must be appreciated fully in order to understand the real significance of modern, automatic systems.

7.2.   Need for Feedback Control

It is difficult for the beginner in system engineering to appreciate fully the role of feedback control.   It is appropriate, therefore, to cite an example, discuss in detail the problems that arise in designing an automatic system without feedback control, and then show the value of feedback control.   In Fig. 7.3a two pipes are shown con-verging in a mixing valve, with a flow of hot water into one pipe at the rate Q_h, a flow of cold water into the other pipe at the rate Q_c, and a flow of the mixed liquid out of the valve at the rate Q_m.   The

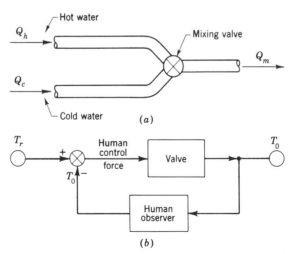

Fig. 7.3   Hot-cold water-mixing control.

purpose of the valve is to provide a means of mixing the hot water and cold water in such proportions that the mixture has a certain specified temperature T_r.

It is apparent that, if the process is to continue throughout the working day, it would be feasible for a human operator to monitor the valve. He would observe the temperature of the mixture continuously, and, if it varied from the specified value, he would turn the valve in the appropriate direction to raise or lower the temperature. This operation is depicted by the block diagram of Fig. 7.3*b*. The reference temperature is T_r, and the output temperature is T_o; the output temperature is observed by the operator, and he compares this with the reference temperature T_r and applies a force to adjust the valve in proportion to the difference between T_o and T_r. If T_o is too great, he exerts a force on the valve to decrease the amount of hot water entering and increase the amount of cold water. The valve, in turn, changes the mixture so that a new output temperature T_o is obtained.

Students frequently object to this method of control on the basis that it indicates poor design of the mixing device. They feel that it should be possible to design a valve that would mix the hot and cold liquid in such proportions that the mixture would have the desired temperature. It is important to discuss this problem in order to point out the reasons for the development of feedback control on such an extensive scale.

In order to examine this situation thoroughly, let us make certain assumptions. We shall assume that the hot water comes in at a temperature of approximately 160° and that the cold water comes in at approximately 70°. If these were mixed in equal proportions, we should have a temperature of 115°. Let us assume, further, that the desired mixture temperature is 125°. Presumably, we could design a valve so that, if it were set at a particular position and if the incoming liquids were precisely at 160 and 70°, the discharge would be at 125°. Let us examine, now, wherein lies the difficulty in the design of such a system. In order that the mixture be, let us say, within 1° of the desired temperature, the temperatures of the hot and cold water must remain within a degree of their prescribed values of 160 and 70°, respectively. If this indeed were the case, the problem would be much simplified. Furthermore, we must inquire into the pressure situation in the two lines. If the pressure in the hot and cold lines remained exactly constant and if the discharge line were open to the atmosphere, we would again have a relatively stable operation, since a single setting of the valve would result in a constant flow from each of the two lines and the rate of flow of the mixture would then be at a constant rate.

We cannot expect that the temperature of the two liquids and the pressures in the two lines will remain constant unless the mechanisms upstream are of great precision; this would call for extremely costly installations in addition to the mixing valve. If the valve is to remain at a particular setting and hold the mixture to a desired value, it again will be a costly device. If we were to assign figures to the cost of the valve and the upstream controls that regulate the temperature of the hot and cold water as well as the pressure in the two lines, we might be able to give a quantitative evaluation of the problem. The cost of the precision valve could be compared with that of a feedback control and a conclusion reached concerning economy. However, the precision valve would have one great disadvantage: If the inputs, pressure and temperature, changed upstream of this expensive equipment, the latter would fail to produce the desired output. Elimination of variation in inputs was the objective of the upstream controls originally. This process proliferates the number of controls, increases expense, and does not solve the basic problem of giving the specified output regardless of input variation. Furthermore, even the best components deteriorate with use and time, thus introducing additional variation in performance.

We consider now the effect of input variation and the role of feedback. Let us assume that the temperatures and pressures in the two lines are not constant but fluctuate by as much as 10 per cent of the pressure and 5° in the temperature, either plus or minus in the case of each of the two lines. We assume, further, that these fluctuations are continuous functions of time, not step functions. Under these circumstances, a human operator would find it feasible to observe the mixture temperature and adjust the valve continuously with time in order to hold the temperature within a degree of the desired figure.

In order to accomplish the same result without an operator, it is necessary to substitute for his ability to read a thermometer a sensing device that produces a signal proportional to the mixture temperature. This signal is then compared with a signal of the same nature but proportional to the reference temperature T_r and their difference is computed. A signal, then, proportional to the difference between T_r and T_o is fed into another component, which produces a signal proportional to the difference and of a magnitude sufficient to operate the valve. This force produces a change in the valve setting proportional to the error in the output temperature. This force continues until the output temperature is equal to the desired temperature. As long as the output temperature has the correct value, there is no force tending to change the setting of the valve. However, as soon as the output temperature changes, a control force is produced to actuate the valve in the direction to correct the output temperature.

This situation is depicted by Fig. 7.3b, where there is substituted for the human being a sensing device, probably electrical in nature, which measures the output temperature in terms of an electrical voltage. The reference temperature again is supplied in terms of a voltage, and the comparator compares these two voltages and produces another one proportional to the difference. This voltage is amplified to a sufficient magnitude to produce a force that will operate the valve.

The adaptability of a system with feedback to changing inputs and the fact that experience has shown their economic feasibility have influenced the design of automatic systems so extensively that feedback control is accepted as standard today.

We return now to the consideration of the human operator to establish certain facts useful in evaluating the performance of the mechanical feedback system. If the operator observes that the temperature of the output is high, he will note this fact and will turn the valve in the direction to lower the output temperaure. That is, he will increase the amount of cold water and decrease the amount of hot water entering the mixing valve. This requires some time, even though it may be very short. In the meantime, the temperature of the liquid entering through the hot and cold lines may well have changed from the value that resulted in the mixture temperature observed by the operator. If this is the case, his correction may be too great or not great enough. In any case, he will shortly observe the temperature again and find that it is still not correct; it may be better than it was before or perhaps not as good. In any case, he will make an additional correction that will be in the proper direction but will or will not be successful, depending upon the input. We see here the significance of the time delay. If a human being could operate instantaneously, the correction would be proper for the conditions obtaining at the instant of observation; this would also require that the operation of the valve and of the thermometer be instantaneous in order that these corrections be perfectly adequate. This cannot be the case in a physical situation, since time is required for all the reactions entering into the operation. In the event that the fluctuations in the incoming temperatures and pressures are such that the correction is too great, a new correction in the opposite direction will be necessary. This observation leads us to the consideration of a combination of circumstances causing an unstable output that is unacceptable.

7.3. Stability

As suggested in the preceding section, certain combinations of circumstances in the operation of a control system can result in an unsatisfactory output. The output might be unstable. It is well at this point to develop a concept of stability, using familiar physical phenomena to illustrate the point.

Figure 7.4 illustrates the idea of static stability in a physical system. The rectangular block (Fig. 7.4a), if acted upon by a force F that tends to raise the left end and turn the block clockwise about the lower right corner, will immediately return to its original position

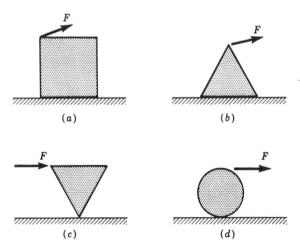

(a)   (b)

(c)   (d)

Fig. 7.4 Elementary stability concepts.

if the force is removed. The weight of the block acting to produce a counterclockwise movement about the lower right support will assure what is called stability. If the block returns to its original position after being displaced, it is statically stable. The triangular-shaped block of Fig. 7.4*b* is also stable in the same sense. However, if this triangular block is balanced as shown in Fig. 7.4*c*, one realizes intuitively that the least disturbing force will upset it and it will not right itself to its obviously unstable position.

The cylindrical body of Fig. 7.4*d* is in neutral equilibrium. If the force F acts, the cylinder moves to the right. When the force does not act, the cylinder moves neither away from nor toward the original position.

In dynamic situations a comparable situation exists. For example, the shaft of a machine rotates at a specified angular speed. If a disturbance occurs, one of several things can happen. The mechanism may restore its original speed. It may stop. It may slow down, then speed up to the original speed, go faster, and even oscillate about some average speed. If the disturbance is ultimately damped out, the system is stable. If the disturbance grows without limit, the system is unstable.

In the ensuing discussion the question of stability will be treated from a physical standpoint, with no effort made to develop formal analytical techniques which are referenced in Sec. 7.7.

Earlier it was suggested that, under certain circumstances, control by a person would be adequate. On the other hand, if his reactions were too slow, it was shown that it might be impossible for him to operate the temperature-control system to obtain satisfactory results. Further, as neither human reactions nor mechanical or electric reactions are instantaneous, perfect control is impossible.

Figure 7.5*a* shows an idealized situation. The temperature of the liquid is the ordinate, and time is the abscissa. At time zero, the temperature is the desired controlled temperature. At time 1 sec, the temperature rises instantly $1°$. The human observer notices this increase in temperature, with a time delay of 1 sec. Assuming, then, that all other reactions are instantaneous, he institutes corrective action which is carried out by the mechanical portions of the system, and the temperature is immediately returned to the desired value in zero time. This would be a nearly perfect control system with feedback. If the time delay due to the observation were reduced to zero,

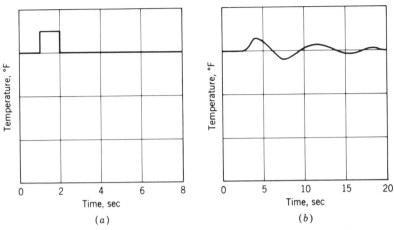

Fig. 7.5a   Response of idealized control system.
Fig. 7.5b   Controlled temperature.

it would then be a perfect system.   The fact that people and machines alike have time delays obviates the possibility of such a perfect device.

Figure 7.5b is a more realistic picture of either mechanical or human control of the temperature of water being mixed by the valve. The temperature is shown rising gradually at the end of the first 2 sec, and at the end of 2 sec more, corrective action has been instituted and the temperature begins to drop.   This drop continues for several seconds until it is observed that the correction has gone too far and the temperature is now too low.   A correction proportional to this error is instituted, and successively smaller peaks are observed in the temperature-versus-time curve, the disturbance gradually dying out.   This is representative of an acceptable control device. The magnitude of the deviations from the desired temperature and the time required to damp out a disturbance depend entirely upon the parameters of the system and the magnitude of the initial disturbance.

In Fig. 7.6 there is a quite different situation.   A disturbance of the same order as that in Fig. 7.5b occurs at the end of 4 sec, and the results of corrective action are shown.   Reaction to the first disturbance rapidly corrects it but then overcorrects it more than the original error, in the opposite direction.   The correction instituted at this time results in similar overcorrections.   This continues with time, resulting in a wholly unstable operation.   This result could come from large time constants in the system.   If corrections are

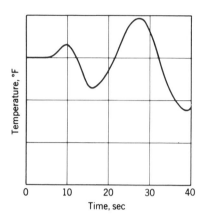

Fig. 7.6 Unstable temperature control.

instituted too late and are of the wrong magnitude, such an instability can develop. The magnitude of the corrections is just as important as the time lag involved.

The time delay is particularly important if disturbances of opposite signs are introduced to the system by the input. It may happen that a correction is too great and should be in the opposite direction. If the system is very senstive and makes powerful corrections for small errors, an overshoot, as shown in Fig. 7.6, can occur.

The essence of the time-delay problem is that a correction that was quite all right at the time of the initial observation may be wrong at the time that it is actually carried out in the system. During the intervening period, the input may have changed in such a manner that the output is not in error or, if in error, the amount or direction is different from that observed when the initial correction was applied. Extreme sensitivity, or strength of correction, causes a rapid change that continues after there is no need for it, and an error is caused in the opposite direction.

Figure 7.7a shows a simple spring-mass system that has been discussed earlier. The stability of the motion of this system is worthy of discussion since control systems similar to it are common, and basic concepts derived from the study of the idealized system can be applied to a real one.

If this system is displaced downward from its equilibrium position by an amount y_0 and released, it will oscillate about its equilibrium position, $y = 0$, within the range of displacement values y_0 and $-y_0$, as shown in Fig. 7.7b, where y is the displacement of the mass M from its equilibrium position measured vertically and considered positive downward, and t is the time. Figure 7.7c shows the same system with an additional force F acting upon it. If F is increased from zero to a constant value F_c by infinitesimal increments such that the system is in equilibrium at all times during the application of F through the final displacement, y will be simply F_c/k, where k is the spring constant. With the constant force F_c applied in this manner, the system will not oscillate but will occupy a new equilibrium position. If, on the other hand, the force F is a function of time and, in particular, if it is a sinusoidal exciting force, $F = F_0 \sin \omega t$, where F_0 is the amplitude and ω is the circular frequency of the exciting force, the displacement y resulting from the application of the sinusoidal exciting force will be quite different from that obtained with a constant force.

If the circular frequency ω of the sinusoidal exciting force F were exactly equal to the natural frequency $\omega_n = \sqrt{k/M}$ of the spring-mass system itself, the amplitude of the displacement of the

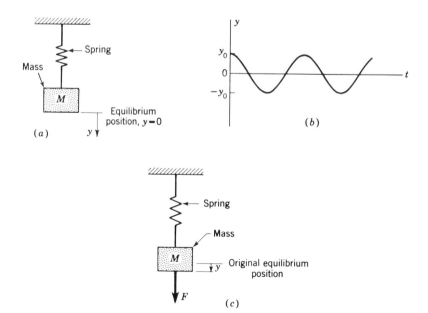

Fig. 7.7 Force-mass-spring system.

mass *M* that would be generated by the application of this force would increase without bound as time progresses. A real system such as this would, of course, have some friction in it, tending to damp out the motion and, under those circumstances, an unbounded amplitude would be impossible. If the frequency of the sinusoidal exciting force is not the same as that of the system natural frequency, lesser amplitudes of motion will be caused. In a system with a mass, a spring, and damping and an externally applied force of a sinusoidal nature, the system displacement resulting from the application of this force will be of the general nature shown in Fig. 7.8, where the system is not damped excessively. The final motion, with an amplitude *A* and a period $2\pi/\omega$, is the steady state that will exist after a period of time has elapsed. Initially, there is superimposed on this steady-state motion a transient oscillation smaller in amplitude and of a different period. The damping in the system eventually eliminates this secondary motion, and the mass assumes a motion with the same frequency as that of the externally applied force.

The relationship of natural frequencies of systems and the frequency of externally applied loads is of basic importance in the stability of system operation. This is closely related to the concept of the time constant, which was discussed in an elementary fashion earlier. If the externally applied force has a frequency matching one of the natural frequencies of the system, there will be forces that reinforce the natural motions during each cycle; this results in an increasing amplitude if the damping is not sufficient to control it. If the frequency of the external force is different from the natural

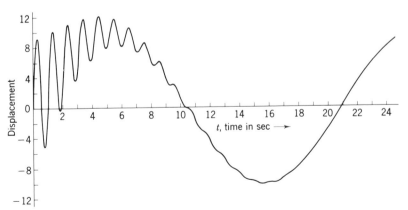

Fig. 7.8   Mass-spring-damper system output: underdamped case.

frequencies of the system, it will sometimes reinforce the motion and at other times oppose it; hence it will not result in an uncontrolled increase in the amplitude.

If a system can be represented by a differential equation that is linear and has constant coefficients, the stability of the system can be determined with relative ease. The simplest form of a linear differential equation with constant coefficients of order n is given below:

$$a_n \frac{d^n y}{dt^n} + a_{n-1} \frac{d^{n-1} y}{dt^{n-1}} + \cdots + a_1 \frac{dy}{dt} + a_0 y(t) = x(t) \qquad (7.1)$$

where the coefficients $a_0, a_1, \ldots, a_{n-1}, a_n$ are constants, $y(t)$ is the dependent variable, and $x(t)$ is the forcing function. The simplest form of a differential equation is characterized by the fact that the highest-order derivative of the dependent variable appears to the first power. A linear differential equation is one in which, when the equation is put in its simplest form, the dependent variable $y(t)$ and its derivatives dy/dt, d^2y/dt^2, etc., appear as linear combinations. To be linear, the equation must contain no powers or other functions or products of these quantities.

The differential equation (7.1) has a complete (or general) solution composed of two parts, the complementary function and the particular integral. First, arbitrarily equating the right-hand side of Eq. (7.1) to zero, one obtains the associated homogeneous differential equation. The solution $y_c(t)$ of this equation is termed the complementary function, and its nature depends only on the coefficients $a_0, a_1, \ldots, a_{n-1}, a_n$. Second, obtaining any solution of the stated equation (7.1) yields the particular solution $y_p(t)$. Obviously, the form of this particular solution depends on the functional form of the forcing function $x(t)$. The complete solution $y(t)$ of Eq. (7.1) is the sum of the complementary solution $y_c(t)$ and the particular solution $y_p(t)$. The nature of the complete solution

$$y(t) = y_c(t) + y_p(t)$$

depends on two features of the system: the forcing function or the input to the system and the parameters characterizing the physical nature of the system as represented by the coefficients $a_0, a_1, \ldots, a_{n-1}, a_n$.

If the form of the complementary solution is such that it approaches zero as time approaches infinity, the behavior of the complete solution as time approaches infinity is determined by the behavior of the particular solution as time approaches infinity. Under such circumstances, $\lim_{t \to \infty} y(t) = \lim_{t \to \infty} y_p(t)$, and if $\lim_{t \to \infty} y_p(t)$ is a bounded function of time, the system is said to be in a steady state. The part of the complete solution corresponding to $\lim_{t \to \infty} y_p(t)$ is termed the steady-state solution $y_{ss}(t)$, and the remaining solution $y(t) - y_{ss}(t)$ is termed the transient solution $y_{tr}(t)$.

For all physical systems the coefficients a_0, a_1, . . . , a_n appearing in Eq. (7.1) are real quantities, and the complementary solution consists of the sum of terms which are of a limited number of forms:[1]

    (I) $c_1 e^{rt}$

    (II) $(c_1 + c_2 t + c_3 t^2 + \cdots + c_m t^{m-1}) e^{rt}$

    (III) $c_1 e^{at} \sin (bt + \phi)$

    (IV) $e^{at} [c_1 \sin (bt + \phi_1) + c_2 t \sin (bt + \phi_2) + \cdots$
$$+ c_m t^{m-1} \sin (bt + \phi_m)]$$

where m is a finite positive integer; r, a, and b are real quantities that are functions of the coefficients a_0, a_1, . . . , a_n; and c_1, c_2, . . . , c_m, ϕ, ϕ_1, ϕ_2, . . . , ϕ_m are arbitrary constants.

The forms of the complementary solution indicated above for the linear differential equations with constant coefficients suggest certain definite conclusions with regard to the behavior of the complementary function as time approaches infinity. If the complementary solution is composed of the sum of terms of the solution forms indicated above and if all the r's and a's are negative real quantities, then the terms in the complementary solution are exponential functions or exponential-sinusoidal functions that all decay to zero as time increases. Under these circumstances it can be shown that[2] the particular solution $y_p(t)$ of Eq. (7.1) is bounded as time approaches infinity so long as the forcing function $x(t)$ is bounded. Therefore, the complete solution $y(t)$ is also bounded, and the system described by Eq. (7.1) is said to be stable. If any one of the

[1] F. B. Hildebrand, "Advanced Calculus for Engineers," pp. 9–14, Prentice-Hall, Inc., Englewood Cliffs, N.J., 1950.

[2] C. H. Wilts, "Principles of Feedback Control," pp. 53–57, Addison-Wesley Publishing Company, Inc., Reading, Mass., 1960.

r's or a's is a positive real quantity, then that particular term in the complementary solution will increase without bound as time increases. This indicates an unstable system.   If all r's and a's are negative real quantities, except that, in one or more terms of form (I), r is identically zero in the complementary solution, those terms will appear as constants in the complete solution.   This system does not fit in either category given above.   It may be classed as the limiting case of either a stable or an unstable system, but often it is classed as unstable for convenience.

On the other hand, if a term with $r = 0$ occurs in the form (II) type of solution, the corresponding term will increase without bound as time increases; thus the system is unstable.   If all r's and a's are negative real quantities except that, in one or more terms of form (III), a is identically zero, in the complementary solution those terms will appear as sustained oscillations in the complete solution. For example, for the spring-mass system discussed earlier, the complementary solution is of this type; namely,

$$y_c(t) = c_1 \sin (\omega_n t + \phi)$$

with $\omega_n = \sqrt{k/M}$.   For all types of bounded forcing function or input $x(t)$, the particular solution is bounded except for

$$x(t) = F_0 \sin \omega_n t$$

It can easily be shown that, for $x(t) = F_0 \sin \omega_n t$, the particular solution is

$$y_p(t) = \frac{F_0}{2k} (\sin \omega_n t - \omega_n t \cos \omega_n t)$$

which increases without bound as time increases.   Whether this system should be classed as a limiting case of stability or instability is a point on which there is no general agreement.   It is, in a sense, an unimportant point, but for convenience these systems may be classed as unstable, or sometimes they are referred to as marginally stable systems.   Finally, if a term with $a = 0$ occurs in the form (IV) type of solution, clearly the corresponding term will increase without bound as time increases, again indicating an unstable system.

It is important to note that the question of stability or instability of a linear system with constant coefficients can be answered completely in terms of the quantities r and a, which are known once the differential equation describing the system under study is given in a form such as that of Eq. (7.1) but with the right-hand side set equal to zero. This is because the form of the complementary function contains all the information relative to the stability or instability of the system.

7.4. Symbolic Representation

Feedback is relatively simple in concept and is represented schematically in Fig. 7.9. The input I is processed through a component which has the characteristic G_1. The input to this device is I, and the output is G_1I, where G_1 is a linear operator, for example, a multiplier or a differentiation with respect to time, as illustrated earlier in Sec. 5.4 as D_t. This input is passed through a measuring element that compares the input with the output. The difference between output and input is known as the error; this is fed into the next processor whose characteristic is G_2. The output from G_2 is the output of the system. The output is observed and processed by the operator H, and this information is passed on to the comparator, which compares G_1I with HOP, and produces a reading descriptive of the error in the output.

Consider now, algebraically, the characteristics of this feedback control,

$$G_1I - HOP = e \tag{7.2}$$
$$G_2e = OP \tag{7.3}$$

Solution of these equations for the ratio between the output OP and the input I yields the transfer function T,

$$T = \frac{OP}{I} = \frac{G_1G_2}{1 + G_2H} \tag{7.4}$$

The analysis thus far is completely general for the system known as a single-loop system or configuration. It should be recognized that the input and the output may not be quantities expressed in the same units or with the same dimensions. However, the input, the output, and the error function are all functions that can be related to

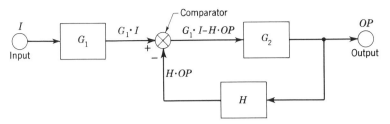

Fig. 7.9 Block diagram of feedback control.

the quantities or units in which either input or output may happen to be expressed. For example, in a house heating system the output is the room temperature. The error-measuring component measures the room temperature and compares it with a reference temperature, which is considered the input. In that case, quantities can be referred to temperatures or temperature differences. The heat loss of the house is proportional to the temperature difference between room and outdoors. The error is the difference between room temperature and reference temperature. The input to the furnace is really a difference in two temperatures translated into a signal that produces a flow of gas. The input to the furnace itself might be considered either a flow of gas, a quantity of heat, or a quantity proportional to the difference between the reference temperature and the room temperature. Thus all quantities can be converted to temperature differences or expressed in units of temperature.

One should not become bogged down in the detail of units of quantities being expressed but, rather, first concentrate on the conceptual basis of a feedback system. In this connection, it is recalled that the purpose of the feedback loop is to make possible the correction of the output of a given automatic device so that the output conforms to specifications. For this purpose, the output of the device is compared with a reference, known as the input, and the output is corrected accordingly when necessary.

7.5. Sensitivity

The electric oven shown in Fig. 7.10 is completely insulated from its environment. Heat flow in and out of the oven at the rate Q is accomplished by an electrical heat exchanger depending upon the polarity of the voltage E across its electrical terminals. For simplicity in this discussion, it is assumed that the rate of heat generated

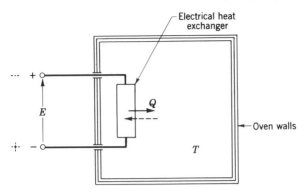

Fig. 7.10   Electric oven.

or absorbed by the heat exchanger is directly proportional to E, that is to say, $Q = KE$.   At a particular instant of time the temperature in the oven is T and the temperature desired in the oven is T_0.   The reference temperature T_0 is a function of time in general.   The temperature within the oven is sensed by a device that converts the temperature reading to a voltage E_h directly proportional to the temperature within the oven, that is, $E_h = HT$.   The reference temperature T_0 is equated to a voltage by a mechanism producing a voltage E_0, directly proportional to the reference temperature T_0, that is, $E_0 = G_1 T_0$.

Figure 7.11 shows the oven and its controls in the form of a block diagram.   The reference temperature T_0 is operated upon by a component producing a voltage $E_0 = G_1 T_0$.   The output temperature, the temperature T of the oven, is measured by an element that produces a voltage $E_h = HT$.   The two voltages, E_0 and E_h, are compared and the difference, $E = E_0 - E_h$, appears as input to the electrical heat exchanger.   If E is positive, the heat exchanger gen-

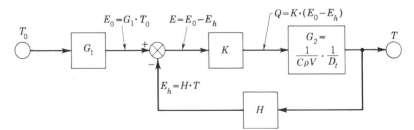

Fig. 7.11   Block diagram of oven temperature control.

erates heat at a rate proportional to E. On the other hand, if E is negative, it removes heat at a rate proportional to E. If the choice of proportionality constants G_1 and H is such that they are identical, then the rate of heat flow Q in or out of the oven would be proportional to the temperature difference $T_0 - T$. However, in a more general form, the physical situation within the oven is expressed by the following equations:

$$Q = K(E_0 - E_h) \tag{7.5}$$
$$Q \, dt = VC\rho \, dT \tag{7.6}$$

where ρ is the equivalent density of the oven material that is heated, C is the specific heat of this material, and V is the volume of the material. Equation (7.6) is simply the statement of the law of conservation of energy. The transfer function G_2 of the oven, excluding the electrical heat exchanger, is the ratio in Heaviside operational form of the output, temperature T, to that of the rate of heat flow Q; thus

$$G_2 = \frac{T}{Q} \tag{7.7}$$

Rearranging Eq. (7.6),

$$\frac{dT}{dt} = \frac{1}{C\rho V} Q$$

Using the operator D_t to replace d/dt, we have

$$D_t T = \frac{1}{C\rho V} Q$$

or $$T = \frac{1}{C\rho V} \frac{1}{D_t} Q \tag{7.8}$$

Substituting in (7.7) for T,

$$G_2 = \frac{1}{Q} \frac{1}{C\rho V} \frac{1}{D_t} Q$$

or $$G_2 = \frac{1}{C\rho V} \frac{1}{D_t} \tag{7.9}$$

In the description of the oven temperature-control system it is clear that G_1 and H are simply multipliers, and G_2 is the integral operator $(1/C_\rho V)(1/D_t)$.

The overall system transfer function is the ratio in Heaviside operational form of the output, the oven temperature T, to the desired temperature of the oven, T_0. This can readily be determined by using Eq. (7.4); thus

$$\frac{T}{T_0} = \frac{G_1[K(1/C_\rho V D_t)]}{1 + [K(1/C_\rho V D_t)]H}$$

or $\quad \dfrac{T}{T_0} = \dfrac{G_1/H}{(C_\rho V/HK)D_t + 1}$ \hfill (7.10)

The expression (7.10) equivalently stands for the following system differential equation:

$$\frac{C_\rho V}{HK}\frac{dT(t)}{dt} + T(t) = \frac{G_1}{H}T_0(t) \tag{7.11}$$

Equation (7.11) will now be recognized as the differential equation of a simple first-order system having a time constant $\tau_1 = C_\rho V/HK$.

In order to evaluate the merits of an oven temperature-control system such as that illustrated in Fig. 7.11, let us consider a particular oven-operating procedure. At an arbitrarily chosen initial time the oven temperature is zero, $T(t = 0) = 0$, and the desired oven temperature is set to be equal to T_0 and kept at that constant value. Using the methods discussed in Chap. 5, the unique solution of the differential equation (7.11) is found to be

$$T(t) = \frac{G_1}{H}T_0 - \frac{G_1}{H}T_0 e^{-(HK/C_\rho V)t} \tag{7.12}$$

From Eq. (7.12) it is clear that there are two lumped parameters, namely, G_1/H and $\tau_1 = C_\rho V/HK$, that affect the detailed behavior of the oven temperature T as a function of time t.

First, we consider the system when its time constant τ_1 is held constant but the ratio G_1/H is varied by varying the constant G_1. In real systems, variation of the parameter G_1 can be caused by the deterioration with time of the component that converts the reference

temperature T_0 into a voltage.   In Fig. 7.12 solid curves show variations of oven temperature T with time for the values of the G_1/H
that are unity, greater than unity, and less than unity.   If
$G_1/H = 1.0$, then the oven temperature T will reach the reference
temperature T_0 asymptotically as time increases.   However, at any
finite time instant, the oven temperature is below the set temperature.
When the feedback control system is designed so that its output is to
follow the input, this difference is termed error $e(t)$ of the system;

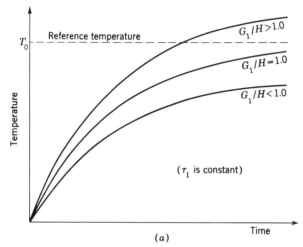

(a)

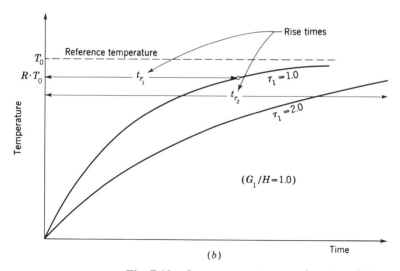

(b)

Fig. 7.12   Oven temperature as a function of time.

thus for the particular oven-operating procedure under discussion, the system error in its general form is

$$e(t) = T_0 - T(t) \tag{7.13}$$

or, using the expression for $T(t)$ given in Eq. (7.12),

$$e(t) = T_0 \left(1 - \frac{G_1}{H} \right) + \frac{G_1}{H} T_0 e^{-t/\tau_1} \tag{7.14}$$

From the expression (7.14), a convenient system-performance parameter related to system error can be obtained. It is to be noted that, as the time increases, the effect of the exponential term in the system-error expression will be unimportant, and for large values of time, that is, for $t \gg \tau_1$, the system error is very close to T_0 $(1 - G_1/H)$. Thus, $\lim_{t \to \infty} e(t)$, which is appropriately termed the system steady-state error and denoted by e_{ss}, is a measure of accuracy of the system with respect to output following the input. In this sense, the best system performance is achieved when the steady-state error $e_{ss} = 0$. For the present situation the system steady-state error is

$$e_{ss} = \lim_{T \to \infty} e(t) = T_0 \left(1 - \frac{G_1}{H} \right) \tag{7.15}$$

It is seen from this expression that the system steady-state error is zero when $G_1/H = 1.0$. This means that the oven temperature can be made as close to the reference temperature as desired if one wishes to wait long enough. This is the best performance that can be achieved.

On the other hand, if $G_1/H \neq 1.0$, say $G_1 H < 1.0$, then the system steady-state error is finite, being $T_0(1 - G_1/H)$. This is interpreted to mean that the oven temperature T can never be made equal to the desired temperature T_0 since, even when $t \to \infty$, the oven temperature will be $T_0(1 - G_1/H)$ degrees below the desired temperature, as can be seen clearly in Fig. 7.12. The interpretation of the situation when $G_1/H \gg 1.0$ can be carried out in the same manner. In this case, the oven temperature will be higher than the desired temperature as time increases indefinitely.

The foregoing discussion leads to the conclusion that, when only the parameter G_1 of the oven-control system of Fig. 7.11 varies, the variation is reflected in the steady-state error. The effect of variation of the parameter H on the system steady-state error can be studied by the use of Eq. (7.15). This effect of its variation will be considered in a later discussion. At this point it is reasonable to ask, "How sensitive is the steady-state error to the variations of the parameter G_1?" A measure of this sensitivity is the percentage change in the system steady-state error, divided by the percentage change in the parameter G_1. Let us consider the expression for the steady-state error given by Eq. (7.15) when the value of the parameter G_1 is increased by an amount ΔG_1; that is, the new value of the parameter is $G_1 + \Delta G_1$. This change results in a new value for the steady-state error, say $e_{ss} + \Delta e_{ss}$. From Eq. (7.15),

$$e_{ss} + \Delta e_{ss} = T_0\left(1 + \frac{G_1}{H}\right) - T_0\frac{\Delta G_1}{H}$$

or $\Delta e_{ss} = -T_0\dfrac{\Delta G_1}{H}$

The definition of the sensitivity of the steady-state error with respect to G_1, which will be denoted by the symbol $S_{G_1}^{e_{ss}}$, yields

$$S_{G_1}^{e_{ss}} = \frac{\Delta e_{ss}/e_{ss}}{\Delta G_1/G_1} = \frac{-T_0(\Delta G_1/H)}{T_0(1 - G_1/H)}\frac{G_1}{\Delta G_1}$$

or $S_{G_1}^{e_{ss}} = \dfrac{G_1/H}{1 - G_1/H}$ (7.16)

Figure 7.13 depicts the variation of $S_{G_1}^{e_{ss}}$ with the lumped parameter G_1/H. In the region $0 < G_1 < H$, the sensitivity $S_{G_1}^{e_{ss}}$ is negative, and as G_1 increases in this region the sensitivity increases in the negative sense. On the other hand, in the region $G_1 > H$, the sensitivity is always positive, and as G_1 decreases in this region the sensitivity increases in the positive sense. Within the immediate vicinity of $G_1/H = 1.0$, the sensitivity $S_{G_1}^{e_{ss}}$ is very large in magnitude, being negative for $G_1/H < 1.0$ and positive for $G_1/H > 1.0$. A physical interpretation of $S_{G_1}^{e_{ss}}$ for the present discussion is as follows: In the neighborhood of $G_1/H = 1.0$ a small relative increase in G_1 will result in a very large percentage change in the steady-state error. The negative sign of the sensitivity $S_{G_1}^{e_{ss}}$ simply

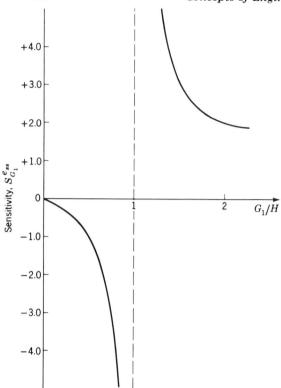

Fig. 7.13   Variation of sensitivity of steady-state error
with respect to G_1 as a function of G_1/H.

indicates that in that region an increase in G_1 will actually reduce the
steady-state error e_{ss}; on the other hand, the positive sign of $S^{e_{ss}}_{G_1}$
indicates that in this region an increase in G_1 will increase the magnitude of e_{ss}.   However, the large magnitude of the sensitivity $S^{e_{ss}}_{G_1}$
in the neighborhood of $G_1/H = 1.0$ comes from the fact that in that
particular region the value of steady-state error e_{ss} is very small; thus
Δe_{ss} itself may very well be small too.   In terms of accuracy of output following input, the large value of $S^{e_{ss}}_{G_1}$ does not necessarily
indicate a large absolute value of e_{ss}.

From Eq. (7.12) it is easily determined that the steady-state
value of the oven temperature $T_{ss} = \lim_{t \to \infty} T(t)$ is

$$T_{ss} = \frac{G_1}{H} T_0 \tag{7.17}$$

Analogous to the sensitivity of the steady-state error with respect to G_1, a sensitivity of the steady-state oven temperature with respect to G_1 may be defined, namely,

$$S_{G_1}^{T_{ss}} = \frac{\Delta T_{ss}/T_{ss}}{\Delta G_1/G_1}$$

It is found to be

$$S_{G_1}^{T_{ss}} = 1.0$$

The physical interpretation of unit sensitivity is simply that a particular percentage variation in G_1 results in the same percentage change in the oven steady-state temperature.

Another important question in regard to the performance of the oven temperature-control system of Fig. 7.11 is, "How long will it take for the oven temperature $T(t)$ to reach a certain specified fraction of its steady-state value T_{ss}?" This fraction will be denoted by R, and for the particular example it is necessarily less than unity. In system engineering it is common practice to choose R in the range 0.90 to 0.95. The time it takes $T(t)$ to be RT_{ss} is a measure of the speed of response of the system and is referred to as the rise time of the system, t_r. With the definition given above, the rise time is determined by

$$T(t = t_r) = RT_{ss}$$

or, by using Eqs. (7.12) and (7.17),

$$\frac{G_1}{H} T_0 - \frac{G_1}{H} T_0 e^{-(t_r/\tau_1)} = R \frac{G_1}{H} T_0$$

or $\quad e^{t_r/\tau_1} = \dfrac{1}{1 - R}$

By taking the natural logarithms of the two sides of the equation above and solving for the rise time t_r,

$$t_r = \tau_1 \ln \frac{1}{1 - R} \tag{7.18}$$

Thus, the rise time t_r is directly proportional to the system time constant, $\tau_1 = C\rho V/HK$, and the shorter the rise time, the faster is the system response, as indicated in Fig. 7.12*b*. In terms of system parameters, this corresponds to smaller mass ρV and specific heat C for the oven material, but larger K and H. The constant K is associated with the electrical heat exchanger in the oven. To require K to be large means that the heat exchanger should be capable of generating or absorbing large flow rates of heat for small voltage differences $(E_0 - E_k)$ that appear across its electrical terminals. The requirements for small values of ρV and C are self-evident for the reduction of the rise time.

Among the system parameters, only H, the proportionality constant of the oven-temperature sensing device, the feedback element, appears both in the system steady-state error expression (7.15) and in the rise-time expression (7.18). If the system output is to follow input accurately, e_{ss} should be zero; on the other hand, if a faster system response is desired, the rise time t_r should be as small as possible. To satisfy both these performance criteria by varying only H may not always be feasible. If the reduction of the system rise time is to be accomplished by increasing H only, from Eq. (7.15) it will be seen that the system steady-state error will be increased when $G_1/H < 1.0$ to start with. On the other hand, if $G_1/H > 1.0$ to start with, increasing H will actually improve the system steady-state error until $G_1/H = 1.0$. Thereafter the effect of increasing H will be the same as stated previously. As a result, the design of components containing the parameters G_1 and H_1 must be considered jointly rather than singly.

The sensitivities of the rise time t_r, or equivalently of the system time constant τ_1, can be determined in a manner similar to that for e_{ss} and T_{ss}. For example,

$$S_C^{t_r} = \frac{\Delta t_r / t_r}{\Delta C / C} = 1.0 \tag{7.19}$$

and $\quad S_K^{t_r} = \frac{\Delta t_r / t_r}{\Delta K / K} \cong -1.0 \tag{7.20}$

where the numerical value of $S_K^{t_r}$ is for $\Delta K \ll K$. The expression $S_C^{t_r} = 1.0$ indicates that a percentage increase in the specific heat C results in an identical percentage increase in the rise time t_r. On the other hand, $S_K^{t_r} = -1.0$, interpreted as a percentage increase in K, results in an identical percentage decrease in t_r.

The effect of component parameters on system-performance parameters such as e_{ss} and t_r, illustrated by the physical example above, can be analyzed either in functional form or in sensitivity-expression form. A careful interpretation of the results will yield much useful information.

A direct measure of the effects of feedback on the system performance can be obtained by investigating the system-gain sensitivity with respect to system parameters. The system gain is defined as the value of the overall system transfer function when all Heaviside operators, D_t's, in the transfer function are set equal to zero. More precisely, the overall system gain K_s is given by a limiting procedure when it exists, namely,

$$K_s = \lim_{D_t \to 0} |T_s(D_t)| \tag{7.21}$$

where $T_s(D_t)$ denotes the system transfer function and K_s is a real positive quantity. In the example of oven-temperature control, $T_s(D_t)$ was given by Eq. (7.10), namely,

$$T_s(D_t) = \frac{G_1/H}{\tau_1 D_t + 1}$$

Therefore the system gain K_s for that system is

$$K_s = \frac{G_1}{H} \tag{7.22}$$

On the other hand, the ratio of the steady-state oven temperature T_{ss} given in Eq. (7.17) to the constant input temperature T_0 is

$$\frac{T_{ss}}{T_0} = \frac{G_1}{H} \tag{7.23}$$

Therefore, from Eqs. (7.22) and (7.23),

$$\frac{T_{ss}}{T_0} = K_s \tag{7.24}$$

For the particular example, the physical interpretation of the system gain K_s is made with reference to Eq. (7.24); namely, the system gain K_s is the ratio of the system steady-state output to the input

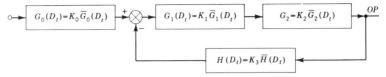

Fig. 7.14   Block diagram of feedback control system.

when the input is a constant quantity.   In complicated systems, the transfer function may contain the nth power (n being a positive integer) of the operator D_t in the denominator as a multiplier.   For those systems, the system gain K_s is defined as

$$K_s = \lim_{D_t \to 0} |D_t^n T_s(D_t)|$$

If D_t^n appears as a multiplier in the numerator of $T_s(D_t)$, then the system gain is defined as

$$K_s = \lim_{D_t \to 0} \left| \frac{1}{D_t^n} T_s(D_t) \right|$$

Definitions of sensitivities were introduced in the elementary oven-temperature-control-system discussion.   We now define the sensitivity of the system gain K_s with respect to a system parameter x as the percentage change in the system gain divided by the percentage change in x, or

$$S_x^{K_s} = \frac{\Delta K_s / K_s}{\Delta x / x} \tag{7.25}$$

Let us consider the simple feedback control system of Fig. 7.14. The four components of the system have transfer functions $G_0(D_t)$, $G_1(D_t)$, $G_2(D_t)$, and $H(D_t)$, with respective component gains K_0, K_1, K_2, and K_3.   Thus, by definition, $\bar{G}_0(D_t)$, $\bar{G}_1(D_t)$, $\bar{G}_2(D_t)$, and $\bar{H}(D_t)$ are such functions of the operator D_t that, as $D_t \to 0$, $\bar{G}_0(D_t) \to 1$, $\bar{G}_1(D_t) \to 1$, $\bar{G}_2(D_t) \to 1$, and $\bar{H}(D_t) \to 1$.   The overall system transfer function of this system is given by Eq. (7.4),

$$T_s(D_t) = \frac{OP(D_t)}{I(D_t)} = \frac{G_0(D_t)G_1(D_t)G_2(D_t)}{1 + G_1(D_t)G_2(D_t)H(D_t)}$$

or $$T_s(D_t) = \frac{K_0 K_1 K_2 \bar{G}_0(D_t)\bar{G}_1(D_t)\bar{G}_2(D_t)}{1 + K_1 K_2 K_3 \bar{G}_1(D_t)\bar{G}_2(D_t)\bar{H}(D_t)}$$

The system gain K_s is then obtained by letting $D_t \to 0$ and is

$$K_s = \frac{K_0 K_1 K_2}{1 + K_1 K_2 K_3} \tag{7.26}$$

From the above expression it is seen that K_s is a particular function of the individual gains of the system components. It is worth noting that K_0, K_1, K_2, and K_3 may, in general, be functions of additional elementary system parameters. The functional relationships that are in question will be available when the individual components are specified in detail. The component gains K_0, K_1, K_2, and K_3 will then reflect the changes in the system parameters by wear, deterioration, or other causes. As a preliminary sensitivity analysis, it is worthwhile to consider the system-gain sensitivities with respect to component gains K_0, K_1, K_2, and K_3.

The gain sensitivity with respect to K_0, $S_{K_0}^{K_s}$, by definition is

$$S_{K_0}^{K_s} = \frac{\Delta K_s / K_s}{\Delta K_0 / K_0} \tag{7.27}$$

where we have considered K_0 increased to a new value $K_0 + \Delta K_0$, which resulted in a new value of the system gain $K_s + \Delta K_s$. By using Eq. (7.26),

$$K_s + \Delta K_s = \frac{K_1 K_2 (K_0 + \Delta K_0)}{1 + K_1 K_2 K_3}$$

or $\quad K_s + \Delta K_s = \dfrac{K_0 K_1 K_2}{1 + K_1 K_2 K_3} + \dfrac{K_1 K_2 \Delta K_0}{1 + K_1 K_2 K_3}$

or $\quad \Delta K_s = \dfrac{K_1 K_2 \Delta K_0}{1 + K_1 K_2 K_3}$

By putting this value of ΔK_s into Eq. (7.27) and using Eq. (7.26),

$$S_{K_0}^{K_s} = \frac{K_1 K_2 \Delta K_0}{1 + K_1 K_2 K_3} \frac{1 + K_1 K_2 K_3}{K_0 K_1 K_2} \frac{K_0}{\Delta K_0}$$

which leads to

$$S_{K_0}^{K_s} = 1 \tag{7.28}$$

Physically, $S_{K_0}^{K_s} = 1$ means that a given percentage change in the gain of the component outside the feedback loop will result in the same percentage change in the system overall gain. We recall that the system overall gain K_s, in our elementary oven temperature-control system, is a factor in the expression that measures the degree of accuracy with which the output follows the input. Thus large variations in K_s cause a lesser degree of accuracy in following, which is undesirable. In some instances the actual value of ΔK_s is of importance; this can be determined only with the detailed knowledge of the system components. In such cases, $S_{K_0}^{K_s} = 1.0$ may not indicate undesirability of the K_0 variation.

We consider now the effect of the gain K_3 of the feedback-element variation on the overall system gain K_s. The sensitivity of K_s with respect to K_3 is defined as

$$S_{K_3}^{K_s} = \frac{\Delta K_s / K_s}{\Delta K_3 / K_3} \tag{7.29}$$

In a similar procedure that was followed previously,

$$K_s + \Delta K_s = \frac{K_0 K_1 K_2}{1 + K_1 K_2 (K_3 + \Delta K_3)}$$

or, by regrouping the right-hand side of the expression above,

$$K_s + \Delta K_s = \frac{K_0 K_1 K_2}{(1 + K_1 K_2 K_3)[1 + K_1 K_2 \Delta K_3 / (1 + K_1 K_2 K_3)]}$$

If $K_1 K_2 \Delta K_3 / (1 + K_1 K_2 K_3) \ll 1.0$, which implies that

$$\frac{\Delta K_3}{K_3} \ll 1 + \frac{1}{K_1 K_2 K_3}$$

or for $K_1 K_2 K_3 \gg 1.0$, it is sufficient to require $\Delta K_3 / K_3 \ll 1.0$; then

$$K_s + \Delta K_s = \frac{K_0 K_1 K_2}{1 + K_1 K_2 K_3} \left(1 - \frac{K_1 K_2 \Delta K_3}{1 + K_1 K_2 K_3} \right)$$

or $$\Delta K_s = - \frac{K_0 K_1{}^2 K_2{}^2 \Delta K_3}{(1 + K_1 K_2 K_3)^2}$$

Now the sensitivity $S_{K_3}^{K_s}$ with respect to K_3 is

$$S_{K_3}^{K_s} \simeq - \frac{K_0 K_1^2 K_2^2 \Delta K_3}{(1 + K_1 K_2 K_3)^2} \frac{1 + K_1 K_2 K_3}{K_0 K_1 K_2} \frac{K_3}{\Delta K_3}$$

or, simplifying,

$$S_{K_3}^{K_s} \simeq \frac{-K_1 K_2 K_3}{1 + K_1 K_2 K_3} \tag{7.30}$$

The significance of this expression for the system-gain sensitivity with respect to K_3 is the fact that it depends upon the product $K_1 K_2 K_3$ of the component gains in the closed feedback loop. In Fig. 7.15 the ordinate is the value of the sensitivity $S_{K_3}^{K_s}$, which is always negative, and the abscissa is the product $K_1 K_2 K_3$. The negative sensitivity simply means that an increase in K_3 will decrease the system gain. Figure 7.15 further indicates that there is a choice in sensitivity $S_{K_3}^{K_s}$, since at least the choice of K_3, and generally K_1, is left for the system design engineer. For finite values of $K_1 K_2 K_3$, a particular percentage change in K_3 will cause a lesser percentage change in the overall system gain K_s. If a system analysis calls for lower sensitivity, it can be attained by proper choice of the $K_1 K_2 K_3$ combination. Nevertheless, only K_1 and K_3 are readily available for the

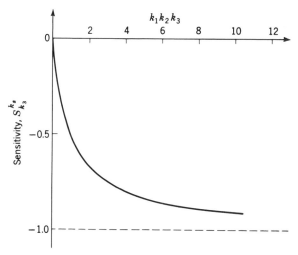

Fig. 7.15 System-gain sensitivity with respect to K_3, related to component gains.

designer's choice, since often G_2 is a plant to be controlled and cannot be altered.

Similarly, the sensitivity of the system gain with respect to K_1 and K_2 can be shown to be

$$S_{K_1}^{K_s} = S_{K_2}^{K_s} \cong \frac{1}{1 + K_1 K_2 K_3} \tag{7.31}$$

In Fig. 7.16 the variation of $S_{K_1}^{K_s}$ or, equally, $S_{K_2}^{K_s}$ is shown.

We now examine the effects of component gains K_0, K_1, K_2, and K_3 on the system gain K_s from the functional-dependence point of view. The system gain K_s is directly proportional to K_0 and is therefore very sensitive to variations in it, as confirmed by $S_{K_0}^{K_s}$ being equal to unity. Furthermore, nothing can be done to reduce this sensitivity. On the other hand, the sensitivities $S_{K_1}^{K_s}$, $S_{K_2}^{K_s}$, and $S_{K_3}^{K_s}$ are functions of the product $K_1 K_2 K_3$. From the functional form of K_s [Eq. (7.26)], this is not obvious at all. On the other hand, from Figs. 7.15 and 7.16, it is clear that larger values of $K_1 K_2 K_3$ increase the magnitude of $S_K^{K_s}$ but decrease the sensitivity $S_K^{K_1}$ or $S_{K_2}^{K_s}$. If it is desired to make all these sensitivities small, one has to make an engineering compromise. Whatever the judgment in this case would be, it is expected that all these sensitivities can be made less than unity in magnitude.

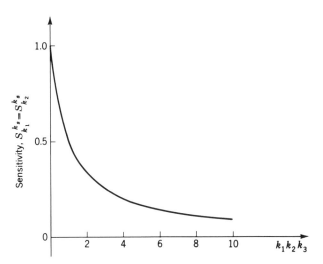

Fig. 7.16 System-gain sensitivity with respect to K_2, related to component gains.

When the control system does not employ a feedback loop, thus $K_3 = 0$, the system gain is $K_s = K_0 K_1 K_2$, and the gain sensitivity with respect to K_1 or K_2 is unity. As a result, without a feedback control loop, any variation in K_1 or K_2 is directly reflected in system gain by the same percentage. On the other hand, when a feedback loop is employed, the percentage variation in system gain K_s is always less than the percentage variation in K_1 or K_2. Thus, from the sensitivity-of-system-gain point of view, this may be considered an advantage of employing the feedback loop.

The sensitivity analysis may be an important part of overall system design. Yet, in actual design, several other system-performance specifications, equally or even more important, must sometimes be satisfied. Their satisfaction will again call for further engineering compromise in the choice of the system parameters.

7.6. Compatibility

The components of a system, or the parts of a component, must be related, one to the other, in such a manner that they will operate without interference and will produce a flow through the system, from input to output, that is properly coordinated and integrated throughout. A very simple example of this, in the case of a component, is the proper arrangement of holes with respect to size and location to ensure the connection of one part of a component to another when so designed. A similar example is the proper dimensioning of a cylindrical hole into which a piston of a hydraulic motor fits. These various parts must fit, one with or to the other, to satisfy the condition of compatibility.

A more general example is a system consisting of both electrical and hydraulic components. Here the requirement that the output of a hydraulic component be compatible with the input to an electrical component is common. At the interface of these two components there must be a mechanism to convert the output of one to an acceptable input for the other. If a hydraulic motor drives an electric generator, the output of the hydraulic motor is the rotation of the shaft and the torque produced by the shaft. This is applied to the driving shaft of the generator, requiring only a simple mechanical coupling between the two.

The output of an electric generator must be compatible with the input to an electric motor with respect to frequency and voltage. If they were not compatible, it might be necessary to introduce between the two a transformer to change the voltage or a frequency changer or perhaps both. The requirement of compatibility introduces the need for careful study of the interconnections of the various components of a system and parts of a component.

7.7.   A Hydraulic Positioner with Feedback

A hydraulic piston that can be used as a positioning device will illustrate some of the concepts developed earlier. Figure 7.17 shows a hydraulic valve and piston. If a force is applied to the hydraulic valve and it moves to the right the distance X_1, the passage connecting to the source of liquid under pressure P will be open in proportion to the distance X_1, and liquid will flow out through the valve into the cylindrical housing surrounding the piston. The piston will be actuated by the liquid flowing into the cylindrical volume and forced to the right a distance X_2. As long as the valve is open, that is, as long as X_1 is different from zero, the piston will continue to move toward the right, actuated by the influx of the liquid under pressure.

This mechanism can be used to position the piston if the valve is operated properly. For example, if we open the valve and maintain it in this position until the piston has moved to some position X_2, we

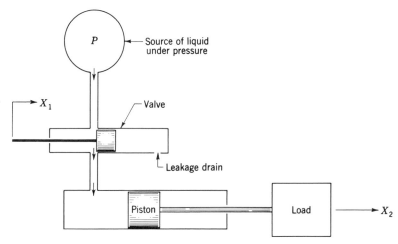

Fig. 7.17   Hydraulic positioner.

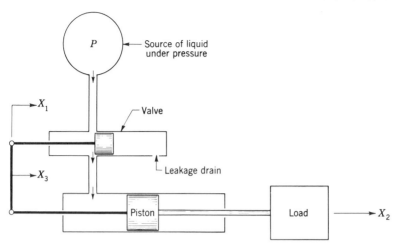

Fig. 7.18 Hydraulic positioner with feedback.

can then close the valve and stop the piston.   However, the accuracy
of this positioning depends entirely on how well the valve is operated.
If the flow of liquid into the cylinder behind the piston were very
slow, for example, if the hole into the cylindrical space were small
and the piston were of large diameter, the piston would move slowly,
and by careful observation we could probably control the position of
the piston reasonably accurately.   However, it would depend upon
several manipulations that are subject to considerable uncertainty.
The fact that the piston has mass complicates the problem, since
there is a tendency for the piston to continue in motion along with
the load after the valve is closed.   Compressibility of the liquid contributes to the uncertainty as well.   All in all, the positioning problem is difficult if a manually operated valve is used.

   In order to improve upon this device, we design a positioner
with feedback as shown in Fig. 7.18.   The valve stem and the piston
rod are connected to a rigid bar.   At the center of this bar a force is
applied.   If the rod connected to the piston is stationary, when the
force is applied, moving the center point the distance X_3, the valve
moves the distance X_1, equal to $2X_3$.   If the piston moves the
distance X_2, the center point, a distance X_3, and the valve, a distance
X_1, the fact that the bar is rigid requires that the following relationship hold true:

$$2X_3 = X_1 + X_2 \tag{7.32}$$

This must always be so as long as a rigid bar connects the three points.

If the valve is moved a distance X_1, the center point moves a distance X_3 and the piston essentially not at all. The distance X_1 is equal to $2X_3$, since X_2 is zero. This results in an opening of the valve, permitting the liquid to flow into the cavity behind the piston. We assume that the liquid is under high pressure and will exert sufficient force to move the piston and load. In this case, the piston will move to the right if the center point is held in a fixed position, a position corresponding to the final position desired for the piston, X_2. The piston moves a distance X_2. This results in a reverse movement of the valve stem so that it will no longer be displaced the full amount, X_1.

In fact, as the piston continues to move while the center point is held firm, the valve finally closes and there is no further flow of liquid. Motion continues until this position is reached, since X_2 moves to the right as long as the valve is open, and the valve will continue to close so long as X_2 increases. This is a positioning tool with feedback, since a position will be reached such that X_2 is equal to $2X_3$. The final position fixed by the piston will be precisely at the distance $2X_3$, provided that the effect of the inertia of the masses and compressibility of the liquid are negligible. Actually, if the rate at which the piston and load move is very high, there would be a tendency to overshoot the desired position described by the distance $2X_3$.

Let us now proceed to an analysis in terms of the feedback method that was developed previously. In order to do this, we refer to Fig. 7.19, in which this system is shown in terms of a block diagram, using the distances X_1, X_2, and X_3. The input is the distance X_3. It is operated on by the process G_1, which simply multiplies it by 2, yielding the value $2X_3$ for comparison with the final position of the piston. The position of the piston, or the output of the operation, is X_2. The sensor H measures this, multiplies it by 1, passes it into

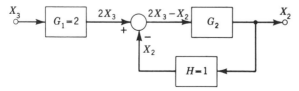

Fig. 7.19   Block diagram of hydraulic positioner.

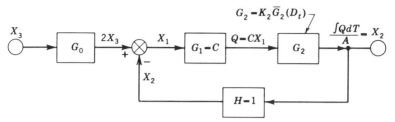

Fig. 7.20 Detailed block diagram of hydraulic positioner.

the comparator which subtracts X_2 from $2X_3$, giving the error $2X_3 - X_2$. This is passed into the processor G_2, which corresponds to the filling of the space behind the piston with liquid. This produces a motion of the piston through X_2 after a period of time. This distance X_2 is then compared with the distance X_3, and the process continues.

The system chosen in this case is purposely extremely simple, in order to keep the analysis and explanation free of encumbering details. A particular simplification is the fact that it yields motion in one direction only. A more complicated device would permit positioning that required a variety of motions.

Figure 7.20 shows the same system as a block diagram describing the processor G_2 in terms of the liquid flow. Into the processor G_2 goes the quantity of liquid Q proportional to X_1, which is the difference between $2X_3$ and X_2, or the error in the output. This quantity Q, equal to CX_1, is fed into the processor, which integrates it; that is, the motion of the piston caused by the flow of liquid over a given period of time produces the integral of $Q\ dT,$ where dT is an increment of time. This quantity, divided by the area A_2 of the piston, yields the distance X_2. We see then that we have a feedback system that yields a positioning of the piston in a manner much more accurate than that possible with a system of the type shown in Fig. 7.17. We consider now the operation of this system in terms of a system analysis, using a mathematical model.

The quantity of liquid that has passed through the valve is equal to a constant times the displacement X_1. Also, the rate at which the liquid flows must be equal to the area of the piston, A_2, times the time rate of change of the coordinate X_2,

$$Q = A_2\dot{X}_2$$

where $\dot{X}_2 = dX_2/dT$ is the velocity at which this piston moves.

From the geometry of the rigid bar, we have

$$2X_3 = X_1 + X_2 \tag{7.32}$$

Taking the first derivative of this expression with respect to time to obtain an equation for the velocities of points 1, 2, and 3, we have

$$2\dot{X}_3 = \dot{X}_1 + \dot{X}_2$$

We know from the conditions imposed on the operations that X_3 will remain a constant, once it is fixed. We therefore impose the condition that $\dot{X}_3$ be equal to zero. We then have

$$0 = \dot{X}_1 + \dot{X}_2$$

Equating the two expressions for Q, we have

$$CX_1 = A_2\dot{X}_2$$

Substituting for $\dot{X}_2$ and rewriting $\dot{X}_1$,

$$CX_1 = -A_2 \frac{dX_1}{dT}$$

Upon separating the variables, integration yields

$$\ln X_1 = C_0 - \frac{C}{A_2} T \tag{7.33}$$

Rewriting in exponential form and evaluating C_0 from $T = 0$, $X_1 = 2X_3$,

$$X_1 = 2X_3 e^{-(CT/A_2)} \tag{7.34}$$

Then, using Eqs. (7.32) and (7.34) for X_2, we obtain

$$X_2 = 2X_3 [1 - e^{-(CT/A_2)}] \tag{7.35}$$

We see, therefore, that X_2 increases from zero at time $T = 0$ to the value $2X_3$ asymptotically with time.

The sensitivity of the system gain K_s with respect to K_2 is

$$S_{K_2}^{K_s} \cong \frac{1}{1 + K_1 K_2 K_3} \tag{7.31}$$

To define K_1, K_2, and K_3, we write

$$G_0 = K_0 = 2.0$$
$$G_1 = K_1 = C$$
$$G_2 = K_2 \bar{G}_2(D_t)$$
$$H = K_3$$

consistent with the nomenclature established earlier in the study of system sensitivity. To evaluate this sensitivity numerically, we must have values for K_1, K_2, and K_3. It has been noted that $H = 1$; hence $K_3 = 1$. The expression for G_2 is found as follows:

$$G_2 = \frac{X_2}{CX_1}$$

but $\qquad Q = A_2 \dfrac{d}{dt} X_2 = CX_1$

But $\qquad D_t = \dfrac{d}{dt}$

Hence $\quad CX_1 = A_2 D_t X_2$

or $\qquad \dfrac{X_2}{CX_1} = \dfrac{1}{A_2 D_t}$

and $\qquad G_2 = \dfrac{1}{A_2 D_t}$

In terms of the nomenclature established earlier, this is

$$G_2 = K_2 \bar{G}_2(D_t)$$

which yields

$$K_2 = \frac{1}{A_2}$$
$$\bar{G}_2(D_t) = \frac{1}{D_t}$$

Similarly, for K_1 we have

$$G_1 = K_1 = \frac{Q}{X_1} = \frac{CX_1}{X_1} = C$$

The area of the piston is A_2 in square inches. Since D_t is an operator denoting differentiation with respect to time, it has the "dimensions" of $1/\text{time}$, specifically $1/\text{min}$.

To obtain a reasonable sensitivity, for example, 0.1, K_2 is evaluated thus:

$$S_{K_2}^{K_2} = \frac{1}{1 + K_1 K_2 K_3} = \frac{1}{1 + CK_2} = 0.1$$

or $CK_2 = 9$

This, in turn, requires flow rates and area related as follows:

$$CK_2 = 9$$

but $K_2 = \dfrac{1}{A_2}$

Hence $C = 9A_2$

If the piston area A_2 is 10 sq in., the rate of flow, C, must be

$$C = 9 \times 10 = 90 \text{ cu in./min/in.}$$

With these values, the time required to approach the final position can be calculated from Eq. (7.35). If we wish to know the time required for X_2 to attain a value of $0.9(2X_3)$, we let the quantity in brackets in Eq. (7.35) be equal to 0.9; thus,

$$0.9 = 1 - e^{-(CT/A_2)}$$

But as $\dfrac{C}{A_2} = 9$

then $0.9 = 1 - e^{-9T}$

or $e^{-9T} = 0.1$

Solving for T gives

$$e^{9T} = \frac{1}{0.1} = 10$$

$$9T = 2.3$$

$$T = 0.255 \text{ min}$$

Under these circumstances, the sensitivity is reasonable, but the time is relatively long for an operation in an industrial process, since the approach to 0.9 of the final prescribed position requires 15 sec, and this may not be close enough for the desired accuracy. An increase in the parameter C will improve the sensitivity and reduce the time required to attain the desired position.

This is an oversimplified analysis since we have not taken into account friction or the inertia of the piston. However, this would complicate the mathematics and obscure the concepts of the feedback control. The general action would be as described thus far, but, in detail, there would be inertia effects from the piston and damping effects from the viscous action of the oil from both the valve and the piston. If this were a high-pressure system, it would be necessary to take into account the compressibility of the oil as well. This would add another complicating factor and place it well beyond the limits of our present discussion. A system including the inertia, damping, and compressibility of the oil has characteristics that would lead to instabilities under certain circumstances; while we are not in a position, at this time, to analyze these, it should be pointed out that the general principles established thus far provide methods that make possible the discussion of the stability of such systems.

The use of feedback in very simple systems has been demonstrated by means of diagrams and elementary mathematical models. These elementary system analyses point the way toward more complex systems. The need for more sophisticated methods of analysis has been indicated. It is clear that the engineering design of an automatic control system with feedback is relatively simple in concept, and if one has a suitable mathematical model, the expected performance can be analyzed. However, in order to carry out such analyses and predictions with more complex systems, it is necessary to become thoroughly familiar with the scientific disciplines that underlie the description of the operation of the various components included in the system. One cannot make a suitable mathematical model if he is unfamiliar with the physics and, in the particular case of the hydraulic system illustrated above, the fluid mechanics involved in the operation and performance of such a system. It is also immediately obvious that mathematics on a much more sophisticated level than that used thus far is necessary to encompass the analysis of the more complex systems.

Stability analysis, particularly, requires much more consideration than is possible in the introduction to the subject undertaken
here. The serious student will find stability analysis challenging and
rewarding. The references at the end of this chapter contain excellent and voluminous material on this subject. Detailed treatment of
stability criteria and techniques has been omitted here, since it is
assumed that the readers will be ready for this material and will proceed to an intermediate-level course in system engineering following
a study of this text. Hopefully, some appreciation of the physical
meaning of the stability problem has been generated by the discussion
at the beginning of this chapter.

Problems

In each of the following problems, design a feedback control
that will accomplish the prescribed task. Describe the control
systems by means of a block diagram and a mathematical
model.

7.1. An east-west highway intersects two north-south highways. Each of these three highways carries four lanes of
traffic. Traffic controls are in existence at each of the two
intersections. They provide for control of the traffic in every
possible direction, including arrows for right turns and for left
turns. Design a control system that will reduce, to a minimum,
the backing up of traffic on any of the highways coming into
either of the two intersections and any tie-up between the two
intersections on the east-west highway. For design purposes,
it may be assumed that there is no restriction of flow away from
either of these intersections. For example, travel to the east
from the intersection of the east-west highway and the eastern-
most of the north and south highways is unrestricted. Similarly, flow to the north from the intersection of the westernmost
north-south highway and east-west highway is unrestricted.

7.2. A mixing valve controls the mixture of fresh water and
salt water in a chemical process. The salt content of the mixture is specified. The required control system must maintain
the salt content of the mixture at the prescribed value.

7.3. In a food-processing plant the product is packaged in
containers, each of which holds a specified weight of the food

product. Several different sizes of packages are produced. Design a control system that will effect the necessary control on the weight in each package and yet be adjustable for several different sizes.

7.4. Delays encountered by customers at supermarkets are very annoying at times. To eliminate some of this delay for customers with very few packages, some stores have instituted an express line, which can be used by customers who have less than a specified number, say five packages, to check out. Other customer-servicing areas have made use of numbers to determine the order in which customers will be serviced. When one arrives at such a service counter, he takes a number, and he is called in order of the number. Devise a control system for a supermarket with five checkout counters. This control system may make use of any method that may seem appropriate to expedite the movement of traffic through the counters. As a criterion for the design of the control system, use the concept that a customer should be in line for both waiting and servicing a time proportional to the number of packages he has purchased and that the time per package should not exceed 1 min plus the number of packages multiplied by 0.1 min.

References

Doebelin, E. O.: "Dynamic Analysis and Feedback Control," pp. 1–24, 196–346, McGraw-Hill Book Company, New York, 1962.

Lynch, W. A., and J. G. Truxal: "Signals and Systems in Electrical Engineering," pp. 648–694, McGraw-Hill Book Company, New York, 1962.

——— and ———: "Introductory System Analysis," McGraw-Hill Book Company, New York, 1961.

Raven, F. H.: "Automatic Control Engineering," pp. 32–49, McGraw-Hill Book Company, New York, 1961.

Sutherland, R. L.: "Engineering Systems Analysis," pp. 158–178, Addison-Wesley Publishing Company, Inc., Reading, Mass., 1958.

Truxal, J. G.: "Automatic Feedback Control System Synthesis," pp. 88–159, McGraw-Hill Book Company, New York, 1955.

Information Processing

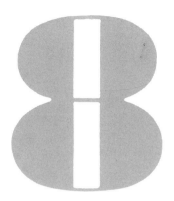

8.1. Problems of Information Processing In the earlier chapters our attention has been concentrated almost entirely on systems that process material or energy or both. However, at various times it has been clear that the successful operation of a system depends upon the maintenance of a flow of information. In a closed-loop system, the feedback mechanism is functional only if information describing the output is continuously available for comparison with the input.

The flow of information in a feedback loop is only one of many examples of information processing that are of major concern. The familiar term "information explosion" derives from the rapid expansion of all human activity, which in turn contributes to the current exponential growth rate of printed material produced to record and disseminate knowledge.

The problem is one in which the processing of information includes storage, transmission, and retrieval. Each of these processes in itself encompasses a wide range of activities, people, processes, and industries; in particular, we associate with transmission of information the relatively new mechanism of television and with processing in general, the computer.

Specific problem areas in information processing which are familiar and yet serve to define magnitude and complexity are data processing in industry, including inventory control and payroll preparation; data processing in banking, particularly check processing and installment loan accounting; government budget control, census analysis, and income-tax accounting; public utility distribution network control; telephone billing; air traffic control; and finally, but not exhaustively, the processing of weather data in the field of meteorology.

The expansion in the need for better means of processing information has been paralleled by improvement in facilities and methods. The high-speed computer and its accompanying means of information storage and retrieval are the outstanding and essentially revolutionary development of the mid-twentieth century.

The solution of problems in information processing has been expedited by the development of a body of knowledge called information theory. This received its greatest impetus from the publication in 1948 of a paper by Claude E. Shannon in the *Bell System Technical Journal,* entitled A Mathematical Theory of Communication. This theoretical consideration of the problem enables the designer to evaluate important aspects of the performance of his information-processing system. The theory relates specifically to the performance of a channel that transmits information, and it establishes the capabilities and limitations of a medium of communication. This point will be discussed in somewhat more detail in a later section.

8.2. Storage and Retrieval of Information

Traditionally, information has been stored in the form of books and periodicals; these still remain the basic media. However, the rate at which periodical literature in technical areas is produced appears to be increasing exponentially with time rather than linearly. This results in a storage problem which ultimately may be beyond the capacity of the conventional library.

To minimize the problem of storage and to increase availability, various devices have been adopted by libraries to improve the efficiency of the storage and retrieval process. Microfilm and microcards make feasible the storage of information in a volume one-tenth to one-hundredth of that required for the storage of books and

bound periodicals. But these devices are not without their undesirable side effects. Material recorded in either of these forms cannot be enjoyed by all readers. However, methods that make possible the rapid and cheap printing of the recorded material give
promise of reducing objections to such processes.

These efforts to improve micro techniques and the reproduction
of the material so recorded go along concurrently with developments
in computing technology, which make available quite new and different means of information storage and retrieval. The storage of
information in computer memories of various kinds is fundamental to
the development of information storage and retrieval systems that
may replace the conventional library. In these systems storage of
information on magnetic tapes, magnetic cores, or drums is currently
available. What future developments will be and what magnitude
of storage and speed of access they will provide is beyond prediction.

The comparative infancy of computer technology leads to the
optimistic prediction that it will be possible to cope with the problems
of information storage and retrieval before the libraries are forced
to the conclusion that conventional techniques are hopelessly out-
moded and the problem is insoluble.

8.3.   Transmission of Information

The transmission of information, or communication, is the branch
of information processing that has attracted the greatest effort of
theoreticians and practical men alike during the post-World War II
period. We shall present here only a brief description of the basic
concepts and elementary examples of the application of the theory in
the practical solution of communication problems.

In order to transmit information by mechanical, electrical, or
electronic devices, it is necessary to establish a code by means of
which the information is put in a form compatible with the devices to
be used. An early and familiar example of a high-speed communication system is the telegraph. Its purpose was to transmit information in the form of messages made up of words. The mechanism was a key that controlled the current in a wire. This current
could be transmitted over long distances, and at the far end of the
transmission line a second mechanism translated the current into
meaningful symbols: dots and dashes with spaces between them.

Since high-speed communication was the basic objective and accuracy of message delivery was the essence of the criteria for judging success, the engineering problem was clear. A code must be devised to provide the fastest possible transmission of the message consistent with the desired accuracy.

It was soon found that, while it was possible to devise a code that effected speedy transmission, the existence of errors was all too apparent. Errors arose from various sources. The operator could send the wrong signal, a malfunction could cause an erroneous signal, and stray currents and distortion of the signal by physical characteristics of the transmission line could decrease the quality of transmission.

The problems then divided naturally into two categories: the encoding problem to obtain high efficiency or speed and the encoding problem to attain error-free transmission.

To obtain high speed on a telegraph, one sees almost intuitively that, to transmit spelled-out words, short symbols should represent the letters used most often and the less frequently used letters should be represented by longer combinations of dots and dashes. The Morse code was devised with this thought in mind, and it is said that the frequency of use of the letters was judged by observing in a printer's shop the number of pieces of type for each letter of the alphabet. It happens that this was not a bad method of design. It is known now that about a 15 per cent improvement could have been effected. Table 8.1 shows pertinent characteristics of the Morse code.

Transmitting words by the use of a code such as the Morse code, with suitable symbols for punctuation, simply by sending each letter and punctuation mark in sequence, does not provide any assurance that the message received is the same as the one sent. In fact, it is a matter of common experience that telegraphic messages of the ordinary variety usually include errors. Fortunately, they are infrequent, and the English language is of a nature that permits reading the message with little doubt concerning the meaning unless a critical letter or number is in error. For example, if the word "house" is transmitted, it is quite serious if the third letter appears as "r" rather than "u" at the receiver. If the final "e" were in error, doubtless the context might make the meaning clear, as indeed might be the case for the error in the third letter.

Table 8.1*   **English Language**

Probability	Letter	Letter	Morse's original code (1837)	Quantities of type found by Morse in a printer's office
0.13105	E	E	⎯	12,000
0.10468	T	T	⎯⎯	9,000
0.08151	A	A	⎯ ⎯⎯	8,000
0.07995	O	I	⎯ ⎯	8,000
0.07098	N	N	⎯⎯ ⎯	8,000
0.06882	R	O	⎯ ⎯	8,000
0.06345	I	S	⎯ ⎯ ⎯	8,000
0.06101	S	H	⎯ ⎯ ⎯ ⎯	6,400
0.05259	H	R	⎯ ⎯ ⎯	6,200
0.03788	D	D	⎯⎯ ⎯ ⎯	4,400
0.03389	L	L	⎯⎯⎯⎯	4,000
0.02924	F	U	⎯ ⎯ ⎯⎯	3,400
0.02758	C	C	⎯ ⎯ ⎯	3,000
0.02536	M	M	⎯⎯ ⎯⎯	3,000
0.02459	U	F	⎯ ⎯⎯ ⎯	2,500
0.01994	G	W	⎯ ⎯⎯ ⎯⎯	2,000
0.01982	Y	Y	⎯ ⎯ ⎯ ⎯	2,000
0.01982	P	G	⎯⎯ ⎯⎯ ⎯	1,700
0.01539	W	P	⎯ ⎯ ⎯ ⎯ ⎯	1,700
0.01440	B	B	⎯⎯ ⎯ ⎯ ⎯	1,600
0.00919	V	V	⎯⎯ ⎯ ⎯⎯	1,200
0.00420	K	K	⎯⎯ ⎯ ⎯	800
0.00166	X	Q	⎯ ⎯ ⎯ ⎯	500
0.00132	J	J	⎯ ⎯ ⎯ ⎯	400
0.00121	Q	X	⎯ ⎯⎯ ⎯ ⎯	400
0.00077	Z	Z	⎯ ⎯ ⎯ ⎯⎯	200

* Taken from Colin Cherry, "On Human Communication," p. 36, John Wiley & Sons, Inc., New York, 1957.

It was stated earlier that the Morse code successfully solved the problem of encoding the alphabet and punctuation and did so almost as efficiently as possible. The effectiveness of such a code can be judged in the light of one of the two basic theorems in Shannon's work. His first statement sets up the limitations on coding for a noiseless channel. Such a channel is free of any disturbances that distort the message being transmitted.

Shannon established two quantities to describe the process of communication by means of a channel such as a telegraph line. The source of the message is said to have an entropy H, which is measured in terms of units of bits of information per symbol, and the channel itself is said to have a capacity to transmit C bits per second. He showed that it is possible to encode the output of the source in such a manner that the rate of transmission over the channel approaches C/H symbols per second but cannot exceed this rate.

We shall not pursue this theorem further but state simply that it opened wide vistas for research; they have been pursued for more than 15 years, and the literature describing the fruits of the research is voluminous. The reader is referred particularly to two descriptions of the bases of information theory which are intelligible to one whose background is no more sophisticated than that of a college freshman, namely, "Symbols, Signals and Noise," by J. R. Pierce, and "Information Theory and Coding," by Norman Abramson.

Shannon's second theorem established the necessary basis for the attack on the second serious problem of coding, that of error-free transmission. This theorem is concerned with the amount of error-free information that can get through an unreliable channel, in contrast to the first theorem which dealt with a noiseless channel. The second theorem tells us that, for any message rate less than the channel capacity C, codes can be found that will assure that the message will be in error by an amount less than any positive number that may be assigned. This yields the unexpected result that it is not necessary to reduce the message rate to zero in order to obtain reliable operation of a noisy channel.

An illustration of the implications of this theorem will complete our introduction to the topic of information theory. Let us suppose that it is desired to transmit a series of digits over a telegraph line. If the series is

101001110

it can be transmitted by using a suitable code in which each digit is represented by a dot or dash, as might be agreed upon. However, this gives no assurance that the list received will be identical with the original. If we repeat every digit and transmit

110011000011111100

we can be reasonably certain that the list is correct if the digits are in pairs. We can be quite sure of the result if we know that not more than one error will be made for each 20 digits transmitted. If the received list were

11 00 10 00 00 11 11 11 00

we would know that the third pair was in error but could not be certain of either the fifth or sixth digit. If we transmitted the digits three times, rather than twice, and were certain that not more than 1 error in 30 occurred, the following reception would locate the error and make its correction apparent:

111 000 101 000 000 111 111 111 000

This method assures error-free transmission but at a very high price. The rate of transmission has been reduced to one-third of the channel capacity.

A much better solution can be obtained by a relatively simple system that includes the transmission of additional numbers but not with simple repetition. For example, the following list of 15 digits will give error-free transmission, if the rate of error occurrence is not more than 1 in 15:

101001110010010

The significance of the last six digits is apparent if we arrange the nine original digits in a 3 by 3 array and sum the columns and rows and indicate an odd or even sum by 1 and 0, respectively:

```
101    0
001    1
110    0
010
```

The digits of the original series are transmitted first, then the indicator digits of the three rows, and finally those of the three columns. If an error occurs in a digit, the location of the digit in error is at the intersection of the row and column that appear to be in error. If a column or a row only is in error, the transmission error is in one of these extra (redundant) numbers, a sum of row or column. Thus,

```
101    0        101    0
011   ①        001   ⓪
110    0        110    0
010            010
```

The circled digits are in error.

These examples are extremely elementary and by no means encompass even a small fraction of the possibilities in coding. However, they can point the way to understanding the fact that Shannon's theory established the limitations; the designer's ingenuity must provide the solutions of the problems.

The transmission of voice, music, and other sounds by telephone, radio, and TV circuits and the transmission of pictures by TV open an enormous and challenging field for the creative designer. In these cases, transmission is not by pulses alone, dots or dashes, but rather also by continuous emission of electrical energy, with modulation (controlled variation) of both frequency and amplitude available to the designer. Shannon's theory of communication is equally valuable in these cases and establishes the bounds within which the designer works.

The demand for high performance is obvious in the radio and TV transmission of music; high fidelity is the watchword. Television demands great perfection as color is added to black and white. Most demanding of all may well be the requirements of interconnected computer facilities that require almost flawless transmission of data between a source and the computer and back to the source again. This transmission over telephone lines is growing and will grow even more as computer centers serving large areas come into being.

The demands for quality are difficult to visualize in some cases, but the very high-speed operation of computers dictates to a significant extent the quality of transmission required. It is clearly not good enough to have a probability of one error per thousand when a computer handles thousands of items per second. Hours of error-free operation are expected; hence probability of error must be reduced to the order of one in billions, and indeed such quality has been attained.

References

Abramson, Norman: "Information Theory and Coding," McGraw-Hill Book Company, New York, 1963.

Pierce, J. R.: "Symbols, Signals and Noise," Harper & Row, Publishers, Incorporated, New York, 1961.

Reza, F. M.: "An Introduction to Information Theory," McGraw-Hill Book Company, New York, 1961.

Elementary System Design

9.1. Design Procedure The design of systems will be illustrated by three elementary examples. In each case, the following steps will constitute the design procedure:

1. Establish criteria
2. Create a mathematical model
3. Establish component characteristics
4. Test components
5. Test subsystems
6. Evaluate system from the mathematical model
    a. Sensitivity
    b. Compatibility
    c. Stability
7. Optimize and redesign

In the design of a real system, the time span for the steps outlined above is large, and certain steps, such as 4 and 5, require extensive programs. In the discussion to follow, simplified systems will be considered, and test data for components, subsystems, and the system itself will be presented in charts, graphs, or other appropriate form, thus effecting a significant saving in the time and space required

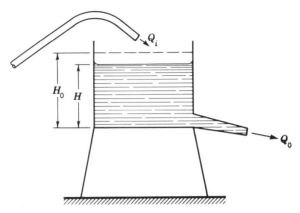

Fig. 9.1   Elements of reservoir operation.

to set forth the procedures and methods that might be employed in such designs, without serious loss in effectiveness.

9.2.   A Simple Control System

Figure 9.1 shows a reservoir in the form of a raised tank, as might be used in a small city.   This reservoir is fed by pipes coming from a pumping station, and it in turn feeds water to the city through a distribution system.   Water must be available in the tank at all times in order to satisfy emergency requirements of the city.   It is also necessary that the pumping system be economical, with neither more nor less capacity than is required to perform its task.   It would be prudent to establish some depth of liquid in the tank, H_0, to provide the necessary storage and assure adequate pressure in the distribution lines.   We therefore specify that the depth of the liquid in the tank should not deviate more than ΔH from H_0.   Since the demand for water varies with time, the outflow is a continually varying quantity. The variation is predictable only in general terms or statistically. The average flow over a long period of time is known, and the daily variations can be anticipated; however, provision must be made for incidents, such as a fire, requiring very much larger rates of flow than occur during the ordinary day.

In Fig. 9.2 a curve represents the daily flow required in the city, exclusive of fire demands.   A method of controlling the flow into the reservoir from the pumps must be selected in order to assure that deviation from the desired depth H_0 does not exceed ΔH. In the preliminary consideration, we shall not concern ourselves with the economics of the pumping station. It will be assumed that adequate economical pumping capacity is available.

In the process of designing the controls, a preliminary selection is made and an elementary analysis carried out to predict performance. The analysis consists of formulating a mathematical model to describe the response of the system to prescribed inputs. If the model predicts unsatisfactory behavior, redesign is indicated. If preliminary studies with the model indicate acceptable performance, design can proceed. We select a mechanism that will measure the depth of the water and compare it with the specified H_0. It also finds the difference between H_0 and the measured depth and regulates the inflow to be proportional to the error in the depth. Another method of controlling the inflow would be to measure both the inflow rate and the outflow rate. The difference between these two is the error and could be used to regulate inflow. However, we shall confine our attention to the first method, measuring the depth of liquid and controlling the inflow in proportion to the error in the depth, since this assures a positive check on the depth, which is of direct concern.

Performance of the system described above will be studied by means of a mathematical model before proceeding to the details of

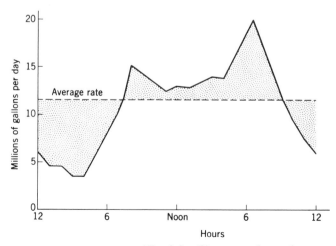

Fig. 9.2 City-water-demand curve.

the design for the specific case.   The system is illustrated in Fig. 9.1, which shows a reservoir, inflow pipes, and an outflow pipe.   The inflow to the system is Q_i, and the outflow is Q_o.   The depth of the liquid at any time is H, and the reference depth to which we wish to regulate is H_0.   We consider first the general case wherein Q_o, the outflow, is not specified but rather may be any function of time. The control regulates the inflow so that Q_i is proportional to the error in depth of liquid, $H_0 - H$.   Figure 9.3 shows a valve-and-float mechanism which operates in this manner.

We shall investigate the behavior of this system in response to a sudden change in liquid depth, which will reveal important characteristics of the control mechanism.   In this analysis we make use of the basic principle of conservation of mass.   We consider what happens during any short period of time, dt.   Liquid flowing into the tank at the rate Q_i will supply to the tank a total quantity equal to $Q_i\ dt$.   During the same period of time, the amount $Q_o\ dt$ flows out of the tank.   Now, since mass is neither created nor destroyed in this process, it is necessarily true that the difference between the amount of mass coming in and the amount of mass going out in any period of time is the amount of mass that builds up in the tank.   We may write this fact in the form of an equation:

$$(Q_i - Q_o)\ dt\ =\ A\ dH \tag{9.1}$$

In this equation, A is the area of the surface of the liquid in the tank and dH is the increment in depth of the liquid in the tank during the period of time dt; hence the volume stored during the time dt is $A\ dH$. Substituting in this equation an expression for Q_i which is proportional to the error in the depth of the liquid, $H_0 - H$, and related to

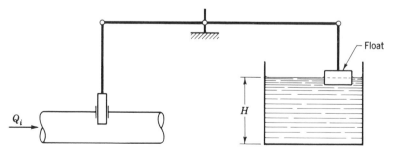

Fig. 9.3   Geometry of float and valve.

it by the constant C,

$$Q_i = C(H_0 - H)$$

and simplifying the resulting expression gives

$$A \frac{dH}{dt} + C(H - H_0) = -Q_o \tag{9.2}$$

The dependent variable is $H - H_0$, and $dH/dt = d(H - H_0)/dt$.

This is nearly in the form of a first-order linear differential equation discussed earlier but differs in that the right-hand side of the equation is not zero. If the right-hand side of the equation were zero, the corresponding solution, for filling the tank with no outflow, would be

$$H - H_0 = C_1 e^{-(Ct/A)}$$

If, at $t = 0$, $H = H_1$, then

$$H_1 - H_0 = C_1$$

or, finally,

$$H - H_0 = (H_1 - H_0)e^{-(Ct/A)} \tag{9.3}$$

As time passes, the right-hand side approaches zero and H approaches H_0 asymptotically. The solution of Eq. (9.2) with terms on the right-hand side different from zero is possible in certain special cases, among which is the one under consideration now, namely, a sudden change in Q_o from zero to a constant. To obtain the solution, we collect the terms containing H and those containing t and write

$$A \, dH = [C(H_0 - H) - Q_o] \, dt$$

This may be rewritten as

$$\frac{A \, dH}{C(H_0 - H) - Q_o} = dt \tag{9.4}$$

The left-hand side of this equation is easily integrable, as is the right-hand side, since the numerator on the left is the negative of the first derivative of the denominator. As a result of integration, the following expression for H is found:

$$-\frac{A}{C} \ln [C(H_0 - H) - Q_o] = t + C_2 \tag{9.5}$$

This may be rewritten in exponential form as follows:

$$C(H_0 - H) - Q_o = C_3 e^{-(C/A)t} \tag{9.6}$$

Solving this for H gives

$$H = H_0 - \frac{Q_o}{C} - \frac{C_3 e^{-(C/A)t}}{C} \tag{9.7}$$

We evaluate the constant C_3 by noting that, at time $t = 0$, $H = H_0$, and we find that $C_3 = Q_o$. Substituting for C_3 in the equation for H gives, finally,

$$H = H_0 - \frac{Q_o}{C} [1 - e^{-(C/A)t}] \tag{9.8}$$

As postulated earlier, $t = 0$, $H = H_0$, and as time goes on indefinitely, $e^{-(C/A)t}$ approaches zero and H approaches $H_0 - Q_o/C$.

Equation (9.8) describes the situation if $H = H_0$ and Q_o suddenly changes in value from zero to a finite amount Q_o. The depth changes from H_0 to a lesser depth and approaches the new depth asymptotically.

The depth H will never quite equal H_0 and will be in error by the amount Q_o/C. We can make this error as small as we desire by making C as large as possible; hence we can keep $\Delta H = Q_o/C$ within prescribed limits.

It is desirable that the system respond rapidly to disturbances such as a sudden increase in Q_o from 0 to Q_o. We shall now consider a method of increasing this responsiveness by introducing into the control a mechanism that will anticipate a change in the depth H. In the mathematical model we introduce a term proportional to the rate of change of H. The rate of inflow, Q_i, can then be written

$$Q_i = C(H_0 - H) + C_5 \frac{dH}{dt} \tag{9.9}$$

If the depth of the liquid changes rapidly, dH/dt is large, and the inflow is correspondingly large. The inflow, therefore, responds to the rate of change in H as well as the error in H itself. This control is said to include error-rate correction. We write the equation for the system as follows:

$$(Q_i - Q_o)\, dt = A\, dH$$

Substituting for Q_i and rearranging terms, we have

$$C(H_0 - H) - Q_o = (A - C_5) \frac{dH}{dt} \tag{9.10}$$

The introduction of the additional term in the description of Q_i has resulted simply in a change in the coefficient of dH/dt. Instead of a coefficient A, we now have $A - C_5$. Effectively, the area of the tank has been reduced insofar as the solution of the equation is concerned. The final equation for H, with $H = H_0$ at $t = 0$ and Q_o a constant, is

$$H = H_0 - \frac{Q_o}{C} \{1 - e^{-[Ct/(A-C_5)]}\} \tag{9.11}$$

This compares with Eq. (9.8) for the simpler control without error-rate correction. The introduction of C_5 in the exponent of e makes it possible to decrease the time required for the quantity H to approach a given value, hence an increase in responsiveness. The smaller the exponent of e, the longer is the time required for H to approach equilibrium. Therefore, if we increase the value of the exponent of e, we increase the responsiveness of the system.

The above establishes certain of the characteristics of a control system for the small city water supply described in Fig. 9.1. Before investigating the detail of the design, we establish design specifications as follows: Five pumps are available, each with an individual supply pipe to the tank and each having a capacity of 1,000 gpm. This tank is one of four supplying the city, and each tank is to have a storage capacity of 75,000 cu ft, or 560,000 gal. It has been decided, on the basis of other studies, that the tank should have an area of 2,500 sq ft and a height of 35 ft. From the demand data given in Fig. 9.2, it has been established that the average flow for this particular tank will be 2,000 gpm. The minimum flow will be 500 gpm, and the maximum, 3,500 gpm under ordinary circumstances. However, it must be possible to supply a peak flow of 6,000 gpm for 1 hr. The maximum permissible deviation, ΔH, of the liquid depth is ± 5 ft, and the desired depth is 30 ft. The problem we shall now consider is the design of a control system to attain the control of liquid depth with a maximum deviation of ± 5 ft.

It is first necessary to establish a feasible concept of the design. In the analysis carried out above, it was assumed that the inlet flow could be made directly proportional to the deviation of the water depth and to the rate of change of depth, if necessary. This requires on each line flow-control valves that would yield proportional rates of flow, depending on the position of a valve. Since flow-control valves of this type are relatively expensive, and five pumps and inlet pipes are available, it is appropriate to consider a system design using on and off controls for each of the five inlets, thus permitting a five-step control, rather than a continuous variation in the flow rate. This would make possible six different rates of flow, namely,

Zero
1,000 gpm
2,000 gpm
3,000 gpm
4,000 gpm
5,000 gpm

It is relatively simple to devise a system that provides for the starting and stopping of the five pumps in response to changes in the depth of liquid in the tank. In Fig. 9.4 an arrangement to attain this end is shown. If the liquid level drops one unit of distance, one pump is turned on. If it falls another unit, the second pump is brought into action, and so on until all five pumps are operating. The increment of depth required to call one more pump into service will be one of the system parameters that must be established in the design analysis. While this system will not give precisely the same performance as can be obtained if the rate of flow varies continuously with deviation of depth, it will not be so different that we cannot use the previous analysis as a basis for predicting certain overall characteristics of the performance.

Since the specifications provide that the maximum permissible

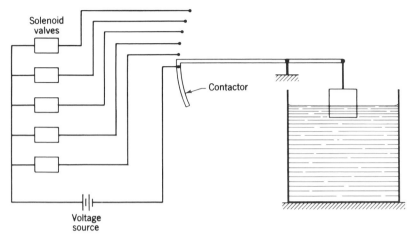

Fig. 9.4 Flow-control diagram.

deviation of the depth from the specified 30 ft is 5 ft, we could start by using 1-ft increments of depth in the pump control. However, we also have the additional specification that we must be able to sustain a peak flow of 6,000 gpm for a period of 1 hr without exceeding the limitation of a 5-ft deviation from the desired depth. The total capacity of the tank, when filled to the 30-ft level, is 560,000 gal, and each foot of depth adds approximately 18,000 gal to the storage. Since the peak flow of 6,000 gpm exceeds the capacity of the pumps by 1,000 gpm, we shall have a deficiency of 60,000 gal at the end of 1 hr. This represents a decrease in depth of about 3.3 ft. This limits the depth increment that can be used for control purposes to about 1.7 ft.

Let us begin the design, therefore, by assuming that we use 0.3-ft depth change per pump, a total of 1.5 ft to call all five into operation. If we refer again to Fig. 9.4, we see that, if the depth of the liquid drops to 29.7 ft, the float will move downward and the arm actuating the solenoid valves will move upward and contact the first control, bringing pump 1 into operation. A further decrease of 0.3 ft in liquid depth will lower the float and raise the control arm to bring the second pump into operation, and so on. The time required for the float to assume a new position as the liquid level falls would be finite but very short compared with the time during which the liquid would fall 0.3 ft. If no pumps were in operation and if the full demand of 6,000 gpm were imposed, approximately a full minute would be required for the liquid level to drop 0.3 ft, with 18,000 gal in storage for each foot. Since a full minute is required for this change in level to occur and since the float would follow the liquid surface within a matter of seconds or less, unless it were forcibly restrained by friction in the system, we need not concern ourselves with the time constant of the float. Similarly, the action of the solenoid valves would be essentially instantaneous compared with the motion of the liquid surface.

In considering the time constants involved in this operation, it should be noted that the demand rate can change almost instantaneously, since large sections of the city may, in a single instant, make increased demands on the water supply by the simple procedure of turning on faucets in homes or opening valves in industrial establishments. One could have, therefore, a step change in the demands on the system, that is, an instantaneous increase in demand. After the demand increased, there would be a lag of roughly a minute, at most, and usually less than that, depending upon the exact position of the float, to call into action an additional pump. The significant time constant in this system, then, is the lag between increased demand and the increase in supply.

To establish the various parameters of the system, we recapitulate and note that it will consist of the following components:

1. A float.
2. A mechanical system to transmit the force from the float to a stepping switch with five terminals.
3. The stepping switch to turn on the solenoids.
4. Five solenoid valves, to be used with 6-in. pipes.
5. A power source for the solenoid valves. In addition, a housing for the valves and switch gear would be necessary, as well as transmission lines from the switches to the valves.

Earlier in this chapter, it was pointed out that there would be seven steps in the design of each of our systems. We have, thus far, carried out steps 1, 2, and 3, namely, selecting criteria, creating a mathematical model, and establishing component characteristics. Steps 4 and 5 are tests of components and subsystems. In this case, it would be appropriate to test the float system and the solenoid valves, as well as the switching gear. The solenoid valves would

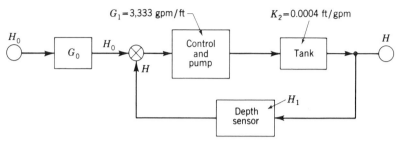

Fig. 9.5 Block diagram of liquid-depth control.

operate or not, as the case might be, and there would be a time constant associated with them, but we have established that the magnitude of this time constant is not consequential, since it is very small compared with the time constant of the liquid surface itself. The response of the float, likewise, is not important except that it produce sufficient force to actuate the switches. Testing in this situation is therefore very simple and does not need further consideration.

Step 6 is evaluation of the system from the mathematical model with respect to sensitivity, compatibility, and stability. Sensitivity of the control system is, by definition, the ratio of the relative change in performance of the overall system to the relative change in a given component. In order to assist in this analysis, we refer to Fig. 9.5. Here the system is shown in the form of a block diagram in which are indicated the values of the parameters G_1, K_2, and H_1, where H_1 is used to distinguish the transfer function of the depth sensor from the depth H of the liquid itself. The value of the transfer function G_1, 3,333 gpm/ft, is simply the rate of flow that has been established by the design specifications when an additional pump is turned on, delivering 1,000 gpm each time the level of liquid decreases by 0.3 ft. The value of H_1 is 1.0. The tank, G_2, has an area of 2,500 sq ft; hence the level of liquid in the main tank will rise at the rate of 0.0004 ft for each gallon per minute supplied to the tank in excess of the outflow. Thus, the numerical value of the parameter K_2 is 0.0004 ft/gpm.

The component gains are defined by the following expressions:

$$H_1 = K_3$$
$$G_1 = K_1$$
$$G_2 = K_2 \bar{G}_2(D_t)$$

The sensitivity of the system gain K_s with respect to the component gains has been shown to be

$$S_{K_1}^{K_s} = S_{K_2}^{K_s} \cong \frac{1}{1 + K_1 K_2 K_3} \tag{7.31}$$

$$S_{K_3}^{K_s} \cong \frac{-K_1 K_2 K_3}{1 + K_1 K_2 K_3} \tag{7.30}$$

The numerical values of the component gains are as follows:

$$K_1 = G_1 = 3,333 \text{ gpm/ft}$$
$$K_3 = H_1 = 1.0$$
$$K_2 = \frac{G_2}{\bar{G}_2(D_t)} = 0.0004 \text{ ft/gpm}$$

Using these values, the sensitivities are found to be

$$S_{K_3}^{K_s} = -0.57$$
$$S_{K_2}^{K_s} = 0.43$$
$$S_{K_1}^{K_s} = 0.43$$

Let us now consider the significance of these sensitivities from a physical standpoint. The gain K_3 is simply a multiplier or conversion factor applied to the depth measurement. It must be consistent with the gain of the component which establishes the measurement of H_0. The sensitivity of system gain K_3, -0.57, with respect to this factor is large but is also dependent upon gains K_1 and K_2 and so cannot be changed independently.

The sensitivities with respect to K_2 and K_3 are equal and indicate the dependence of the system upon the tank area and number of pumps employed to correct the water level. Since the tank area is specified and not subject to the designer's control, K_2 is fixed. The numerical value of K_1 is established by the number of pumps called into play per unit of change in depth error $(H_0 - H)$. If more pumps are used or, stated conversely, if a smaller depth change calls for an additional pump, K_1 is increased and the sensitivity decreased. This means, for example, that a deterioration of the pump performance would be less disturbing if more pumps are used to correct a given depth deficiency. It would be possible to improve the sensitivity with respect to both K_1 and K_2 by increasing K_1. However, the stability of the system should then be examined to be certain that it is adequate and not disturbed by the increase in the gain K_1.

Compatibility requires that we consider the relationships between the outputs of the various components and their corresponding inputs. Since the outputs of G_0 and H_1 are added directly, they must be in the same units. This is taken care of since the float measures H and this is transmitted through the arm to actuate the switches. The zero setting of this arm, which determines when the first switch will be turned on, is the measurement of H_0. Consequently, the location of the switch control arm determines H_0 and its motion measures H; these are compatible in this system since each is a displacement of the control arm. The output of the adder is simply the signal that controls the flow of the pumps. The pumps deliver water to the tank, which is, of course, compatible with the design, since we desire to have water in the tank, and the output of the entire system is the depth of liquid, which is compatible with the design. In fact, the compatibility considerations in this particular design are trivial. Inherent in the design of H_1 and G_0 is the requirement that the voltage of the current source, the electrical wiring, and the switches be compatible with the requirements of the solenoid valves.

The stability of this system can be discussed first in terms of the equations that were written in creating the mathematical model and the solutions obtained. The solutions indicated no inherent instability in the system when the rate of flow is proportional to the deviation from the desired depth. In the actual design we have introduced one additional consideration not implied in the mathematical model, namely, the on-off operation and the finite increments in the rate of flow, which in turn result in a time delay between the change in depth and the sensing of this change.

Time delays can introduce instabilities, and we shall now investigate the effect of the time delay on the performance of the system. Instability would be encountered in this system with on-off controls if a drop in liquid level were followed by a response that brought the pumps into action in such a manner that the depth built up too rapidly and exceeded desirable limits before another response to the depth measurement resulted in a decrease in flow. Alternatively, if the response to a change in depth failed to bring the pumps into action quickly enough, the liquid level could drop excessively

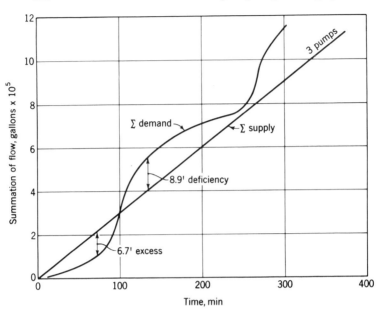

Fig. 9.6 Mass diagram of variable demand with constant supply.

and might not be recoverable if the demand exceeded pump capacity.

In Fig. 9.6 the abscissa is the time, and the ordinate is the summation of either the inflow to the tank or the outflow from the tank. Considering the line marked demand, we see that the summation indicates considerable variability in the outflow from the beginning of the time measurement until the end. The ordinate represents the accumulated flow. The accumulation of outflow alone does not have a direct physical significance. However, an inflow curve, as, for example, the one marked "three pumps," indicates the accumulated flow from three pumps operating continuously. They would pump a total of 300,000 gal in 100 min, as shown. If these three pumps had been operating continuously, the outflow would, at times, have been sufficient to drain the tank down, and at other times there would have been an excess of inflow. At the end of 75 min, there would have been an excess of 6.7 ft of depth in the tank. After 132 min, there would have been an 8.9-ft deficiency. This would not have been satisfactory operation in terms of the specified performance.

If the controls that we have selected are in operation, the result will be as shown in Fig. 9.7. We assume that at time zero the liquid is at the control depth H_0. At the end of approximately 4 min, the net outflow accumulates to the extent that there is a deficiency of 0.3 ft in the depth. The first pump is turned on; this continues until the end of 9 min. At that point the surface of the liquid has dropped 0.6 ft, and the second pump is called into action. Very shortly thereafter the third, fourth, and fifth pumps are called upon so that at the end of approximately 11 min total elapsed time all five pumps are operating. They continue in operation until about $17\frac{1}{2}$ min have elapsed, during which the surface rises sufficiently to justify shutting off one pump. At the end of $19\frac{1}{2}$ min another is shut off; at the end of $23\frac{1}{3}$, another, and operation continues with two pumps until about $25\frac{1}{2}$ min have elapsed, at which time a rapid drop in the water surface again takes place and all five pumps are called into service.

During the period from 12 to 13 min, the surface drops approximately 1.8 ft, which is the maximum deficiency during the 30-min period shown in Fig. 9.7. So long as the demand on the tank does not exceed 5,000 gpm, the water surface will always remain within 1.5 ft of the desired 30-ft depth. Since the valves respond almost instantaneously compared with the time required for an incremental raise in the surface, there will be no tendency for the water surface to rise above the 30-ft level under any circumstances.

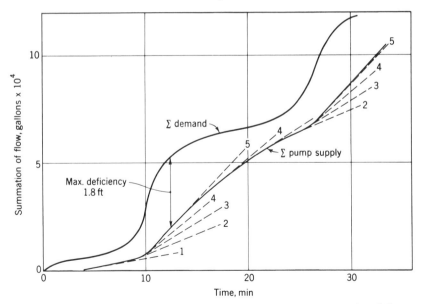

Fig. 9.7 Mass diagram with regulated flow.

Since the system cannot overshoot the 30-ft level and if the demand does not exceed 5,000 gpm, the water will not be more than 1.5 ft below the 30-ft level, an elevation of 28.5 above the bottom of the tank; the operation is stable within this range, oscillating in response to the demand on the system. If the increments that call a new pump into action were smaller, the oscillation would be smaller and the deficiency below the 30-ft level would be smaller. However, the stability would be equally good.

We see, then, that this system has reasonable sensitivity, it is stable, and no great difficulty is encountered in making the various components compatible. It remains, therefore, to investigate the adequacy of the design from the standpoint of cost or other criterion with respect to which optimization might be desirable.

The optimization problem in this particular design is comparatively elementary. There is no need to employ formal analytical procedures of great complexity. This is the case in the design of many relatively simple systems. It is not good practice to use elaborate methods when a straightforward approach yields the desired results. All the conditions imposed by the design specifications have been met, and none leaves opportunities for optimization, since deviations of the depths and the maximum demand on the system are specified. The matter of cost remains to be considered, and, within the framework of the design selected, economies could be effected in the choice of components. The use of solenoid valves establishes the general design of the control system; within that framework, optimization with respect to cost would be simply a matter of selecting the valves that would give the minimum cost and still satisfy the specifications.

An alternative design should be considered if economy is deemed a matter of real concern. One alternative design employs valves controlled by hydraulic pressure rather than by electric energy. If this were considered, it would be a matter of comparing the cost of the electrical system and the hydraulic system and then selecting the one that gave the greater economy. However, when comparing two systems as different as an electrical and a hydraulic system, it is necessary to place some value on various features of performance since the cost differential in itself might not be sufficient for a wise decision. A hydraulic system would require a source of high-pressure hydraulic fluid and a distribution system for this fluid. The electrical system would have the advantage that it could use electric energy supplied from the public utility system and would need no auxiliary source of power, as does the hydraulic system.   With reference to reliability, both systems rely on the public supply of electric energy; hence safety should be considered, but neither would offer any particular advantage in this respect.

A third system would be a pneumatic system, which would have a real advantage in that compressed air could be stored and used for the operation of the valves, even in case of an emergency that cut off the supply of electric power.   A comparison, then, of the three systems—hydraulic, pneumatic, and electrical—would constitute the optimization problem.

The major feature of this optimization problem would be the establishment of criteria for judgment.   The cost of the components and installation alone would not be decisive.   Undoubtedly, one of the systems would be significantly cheaper than the others; if this were the only criterion, the matter would be settled.   However, if value were placed on reliability under adverse conditions, such as major disaster, it might be that the pneumatic system would have real advantages, since it could operate and maintain fire-fighting capacity longer than the other two systems.   Cost of maintenance also enters the optimization procedure.

Other systems are possible, and if these were designed and costs obtained, they should be considered along with the three suggested above.

The evaluation of the control system could be carried out by means of the mathematical model in much the same way as in the discussion above, imposing any desired demand curve on the system and evaluating performance.   After the system had been assembled, it would be tested to determine the quality of the components and the effectiveness of the control system under operating conditions.   A complete evaluation under these conditions would take a very long time and, in the case of this system, would not likely reveal anything not already anticipated from the model.   This would not necessarily be true of a more complex system.

9.3.   A House Heating-control System

The liquid-level control system is analogous to a heating system for use in a family dwelling.   Figure 9.8 shows the latter system in a

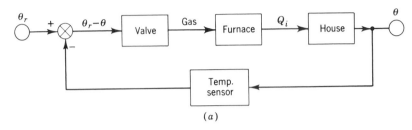

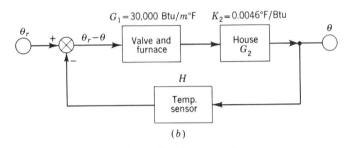

Fig. 9.8   Block diagram of house heating-control system.

block diagram similar to that of Fig. 9.5.   In fact, the similarity is essentially complete.   The house is analogous to the tank; the furnace is analogous to the pump; the valve on the gas line is analogous to the pump control or the valve of the previous system; the temperature-sensing device is comparable to the depth sensor.   Here we compare the difference between the temperature θ, sensed in the house, and the reference temperature θ_r, which is the desired house temperature.   The difference between these two, the error in the temperature, is measured and fed to a valve that controls the flow of gas to the furnace; the furnace produces heat, which is introduced to the house at the rate Q_i; the house loses heat at the rate Q_o.   If insufficient heat is supplied to the house, the temperature θ falls.   If the amount of heat going into the house exceeds that flowing out by natural means, the temperature of the house will rise.   The purpose of the feedback mechanism is to keep the difference between the reference temperature θ_r and the temperature of the house near zero. An important difference between the two systems is that, while a negative demand for water is impossible, a high outdoor temperature with a resultant heat flow into the house is possible.

The use of a mathematical model and formal design procedures in planning a common house-heating system can seldom be justified. The design procedure is quite routine. However, there are two reasons for using it as an example. First, the system is a familiar one, easily understood by the reader, and furnishes a good example of the type of system under consideration. Secondly, the failure to use such a method and a mathematical model in the early days of the design of floor-radiant heating systems resulted in considerable delay and misunderstanding that could have been avoided. The value of a formal design procedure was thus established, although at a high price.

The floor-radiant heating system depends upon the floor as the source of heat for the living area. The floor slab is heated by coils or ducts which carry hot air or liquid. The fact that the mass of the floor is large and stores a great deal of heat can be very undesirable when a cold night is followed by a rapid rise in outdoor temperature during the day. The energy stored in the slab heats the house excessively during the day, making for great discomfort. Similarly, if the outdoor temperature drops rapidly, the thermal inertia resists rapid heating of the slab and the living area is too cold. All this would have been apparent from a simple mathematical model of the situation if it had been used before construction began.

Beginning now with the house itself, the rate at which heat flows out, Q_o, is dependent upon several things: the interior temperature θ; the exterior temperature θ_o; the insulating properties of the walls, floors, and ceilings of the house; and the leakage of air through cracks, open doors, and windows. If the temperature difference $\theta - \theta_o$ is large, the rate at which heat flows out of the house will be correspondingly large. In fact, the rate at which heat flows out through walls, ceilings, and floors can be represented by the equation $Q_o = UA(\theta - \theta_o)$, where U is the rate at which heat flows per unit area per degree temperature difference; the quantity A is the area of floors, walls, and ceilings through which the heat flows; and θ and θ_o were defined previously.

The linear relationship between heat flow and temperature difference is adequate for the case in hand. The rate at which heat flows into the house, Q_i, is dependent upon the rate at which gas is supplied to the furnace and the efficiency with which the furnace makes use of the heating value of the gas in producing the heated medium that flows into the house. If this system controls the rate of flow of gas in proportion to the temperature difference, we must provide a valve to assure that the rate of flow is proportional to temperature difference. If, on the other hand, an on-off system is adequate, we need provide only a valve that will turn on the gas when the temperature θ drops below some specified value and will turn it off again when θ rises to another specified value.

The mathematical model for the house heating system is similar to that of the tank and water-level control of the previous section. However, it differs in one important respect: The outflow is proportional to the difference between the indoor and outdoor temperatures.

Since we shall use an on-off system, it is necessary to consider two different situations in the analysis by means of the mathematical model. In one, the heater is on and the temperature in the house is below the control temperature; in the other, the heater is off and the temperature is initially above or equal to the control temperature. We proceed, then, as follows: With the heater on, the heat inflow Q_i is a constant. We then write

$$(Q_i - Q_o)\, dt = \rho c V\, d\theta \tag{9.12}$$

where ρ is the average density of the material to be heated, c is the specific heat of this material, and V is its volume. All other terms are as defined previously. The solution of Eq. (9.12) proceeds as follows:

$$\frac{d\theta}{Q_i - Q_o} = \frac{1}{\rho c V}\, dt$$

but the heat loss Q_o is given by

$$Q_o = U(\theta - \theta_o)$$

Hence $\dfrac{d\theta}{Q_i - U(\theta - \theta_o)} = \dfrac{1}{\rho c V}\, dt$

Since the derivative of $Q_i - U(\theta - \theta_o)$ with respect to the temperature θ is

$$\frac{d}{d\theta}[Q_i - U(\theta - \theta_o)] = -U \tag{9.13}$$

Eq. (9.13) can be put into a form for integration directly by multiplying numerator and denominator of the left-hand side by $-U$; thus,

$$\frac{-U \, d\theta}{-U[Q_i - U(\theta - \theta_o)]} = \frac{dt}{\rho c V}$$

Integration of both sides gives

$$-\frac{1}{U} \ln [Q_i - U(\theta - \theta_o)] = \frac{1}{\rho c V} t + c_1 \tag{9.14}$$

provided θ_o is a constant also. To evaluate c_1, we assume that initially at $t = 0$ the inside temperature was θ_1, which is less than the reference temperature and calls for heat, thus establishing the heat flow Q_i. Hence

$$-\frac{1}{U} \ln [Q_i - U(\theta_1 - \theta_o)] = c_1$$

Substitution in (9.14) yields

$$-\frac{1}{U} \ln \frac{Q_i - U(\theta - \theta_o)}{Q_i - U(\theta_1 - \theta_o)} = \frac{t}{\rho c V} \tag{9.15}$$

Rewriting in exponential form,

$$Q_i - U(\theta - \theta_o) = [Q_i - U(\theta_1 - \theta_o)]e^{-(Ut/\rho c V)}$$

Rearranging terms and solving for temperature difference,

$$\theta - \theta_o = \frac{Q_i}{U} - \left[\frac{Q_i}{U} - (\theta_1 - \theta_o) \right] e^{-(Ut/\rho c V)}$$

Finally,

$$\theta = \theta_o + \frac{Q_i}{U} - \left[\frac{Q_i}{U} + (\theta_o - \theta_1) \right] e^{-(Ut/\rho c V)} \tag{9.16}$$

Equation (9.16) tells us that, with the heater on and starting initially with an indoor temperature of θ_1, this temperature will rise and asymptotically approach the temperature $Q_i/U + \theta_o$. However, in actuality, the control will stop the heater when the indoor temperature reaches θ_c, the control temperature, and for all practical purposes this stoppage can be considered instantaneous compared with the time required for the temperature to rise a few degrees.

That the final equilibrium indicated by Eq. (9.16) is reasonable can be shown as follows: If a long time has elapsed after the furnace started, the term $e^{-(Ut/\rho cV)}$ is very small; hence, approximately,

$$\theta = \theta_o + \frac{Q_i}{U}$$

or $Q_i = U(\theta - \theta_o)$ (9.17)

This states that the heat loss of the house, $U(\theta - \theta_o)$, is equal to the heat input from the furnace, Q_i, a stable condition.

With the heater off, Q_i is equal to zero.   The heat balance is given by Eq. (9.12).   The solution of this equation is obtained as follows: Eq. (9.12) with $Q_i = 0$ yields

$$-Q_o \, dt = \rho c V \, d\theta \tag{9.18}$$

or, since $Q_o = U(\theta - \theta_o)$,

$$-U(\theta - \theta_o) \, dt = \rho c V \, d\theta$$

and $$\frac{d\theta}{-U(\theta - \theta_o)} = \frac{1}{\rho c V} \, dt$$

Integration yields

$$-\frac{1}{U} \ln (\theta - \theta_o) = \frac{t}{\rho c V} + c_2 \tag{9.19}$$

At $t = 0$, $\theta = \theta_2$; therefore,

$$c_2 = -\frac{1}{U} \ln (\theta_2 - \theta_o)$$

and finally, in exponential form,

$$\theta = \theta_o + (\theta_2 - \theta_o)e^{-(Ut/\rho cV)} \tag{9.20}$$

Equation (9.20) indicates that, with the heater off and an indoor temperature initially θ_2, the temperature indoors will fall and ap-

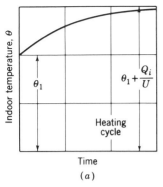
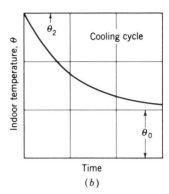

Fig. 9.9 Temperature-time graphs for house heating system.

proach the outdoor temperature asymptotically. This drop is indicated in Fig. 9.9b, where it can be compared with the temperature rise given by Eq. (9.16) in Fig. 9.9a.

These two characteristics are combined in Fig. 9.10 to show the scheme of things with an outdoor temperature θ_0 equal to 20°F, an indoor control temperature θ_c equal to 70°, and a control interval of 4°. When the temperature drops to 68°, the furnace turns on; when it rises to 72°, it turns off. The solution of the equations, which are the mathematical models of this system, indicates a stable system under the circumstances of a constant outdoor temperature. There is an oscillation in the indoor temperature, but it is within narrowly confined limits, and these limits can be made as narrow as desired.

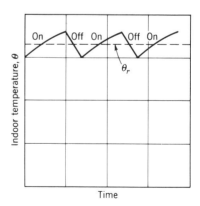

Fig. 9.10 House temperature-time diagram with on-off control.

In the event that the outdoor temperature fluctuates, this oscillation would be superimposed on the indoor temperature as well. However, no instability would be introduced unless the outdoor temperature rose above the indoor control temperature of 72°. It would then be impossible for the heater to control the indoor temperature and maintain it less than 72°. If the system were to combine an air-conditioning and heating system, such control would be possible. If the temperature were oscillating outdoors in the neighborhood of 70°, ±2°, undesirable fluctuations in operation from heater to air conditioner would be possible.

If the outdoor temperature drops so low that the capacity of the furnace is inadequate, the indoor temperature will fall below 68° and the furnace will continue to operate. The limiting outdoor temperature at which the furnace can maintain an indoor temperature of 68° is given by

$$Q_i = U(68 - \theta_o)$$

or $\quad \theta_o = 68 - \dfrac{Q_i}{U}$ $\hspace{4cm}$ (9.21)

We next consider the sensitivity of the system. However, in order to do this, it will be necessary to make a preliminary selection of a heater and control devices in order that we can have orders of magnitude for computing transfer functions.

This house heating system requires a furnace and valve, a temperature-sensing device, and a means of turning the valve on and off. To establish the capacity of the furnace, we examine the quantities of heat involved in heating the house. The floor area is 1,600 sq ft, the wall area is 1,300 sq ft, and, correspondingly, the ceiling has an area of 1,600 sq ft. For the walls and ceiling we select a value of $U = 0.3$ Btu/(sq ft)(°F) temperature difference, and for the floor the corresponding value is 0.1. For design purposes, the temperature difference between inside and outside temperature is 50°F. A difference of 20° between inside and ground temperature for the floor will be used.

The heat loss of the house, represented by average values of the rate of heat flow through the walls, floors, and ceilings, is an approximation. The windows represent a very significant factor in heat loss, with a flow of heat outward at a much greater rate than through the walls or the ceiling. In addition, doors will be opened on occasion, admitting cold air. However, for the purposes of this elementary design, we shall neglect these factors, recognizing, as we do so, that they would be a real influence in an actual design.

If we carry out the calculations for the quantity of heat flowing out through the walls, the ceilings, and the floors, when the inside temperature is at the design point, we find that we have a total heat loss of 46,700 Btu/hr. We must therefore provide a furnace with a capacity of at least this much; in fact, we should be well advised to supply one with a capacity of 60,000 to 70,000 Btu/hr, in view of the neglected factors noted above and the reserve capacity needed to secure rapid adjustments in temperature.

We investigate now the sensitivity required in the temperature-sensing device and the magnitude of time intervals as temperature falls and rises between prescribed limits. For the purpose of providing comfort, it might be well to limit the total change in temperature to about 3 or 4° at the maximum. If we desire a room temperature of 70°, we should not permit it to fall below 68° nor, in general, to rise above 72° when the furnace is in operation. Using this range, we can make a rough determination of the capacity the furnace should have if the maximum demand is 46,700 Btu/hr and the temperature drops 2° in the house. The furnace goes on, and we wish to raise the temperature 4° in a reasonable period of time. If the furnace had no capacity in excess of 46,700 Btu/hr, it would never raise the temperature above 68°. However, if it has a very large capacity, the temperature could be raised very rapidly. The calculation of orders of magnitude follows.

With the floor area of 1,600 sq ft, we assume an 8-ft ceiling and a total volume, therefore, of 12,800 cu ft of air that must be heated by the furnace. The specific heat of air can be taken as 0.24 Btu/(cu ft) (°F) and the density 0.07 lb/cu ft. Multiplying these three quantities together, we find that 218 Btu is required to raise the temperature of the air in the house 1°F. If we wish to raise the temperature 4°, 872 Btu is required. If we wish to raise the temperature 4° in a period of time T, we should divide 872 by this time T to determine the excess capacity that the furnace must have above the minimum of 46,700 Btu/hr. Let us assume then, simply for design purposes, that we wish to spend no more than 5 min in raising the temperature 4°. Since 5 min is $\frac{1}{12}$ hr, we would require 12×872, or 10,500 Btu/hr excess capacity to perform this feat. This requires a total furnace capacity of 57,200 Btu/hr, comparable to the 60,000 to 70,000 Btu/hr suggested earlier.

In this portion of the analysis, certain simplifications have been made; a very important one is that the temperature has been assumed to be uniform throughout the house. The heat content of the heated air would not be distributed instantaneously nor uniformly throughout the living area; hence the temperature would not be uniform. If heated air is introduced to a room through an opening in the wall or floor, as the case may be, the air comes in at a high velocity and distributes itself throughout the room in a manner dependent upon the mechanics of the situation. However, this is a recognized simplification that we must keep in mind when we carry through the design and realize that our idealization will not be attained in the actual case.

The order of magnitude of one of the time constants, namely, the 5 min required to raise the temperature from the lower limit to the upper limit, has been established and can be used in determining the sensitivity and time constant of other devices in the system. For example, the temperature-sensing device need not have extraordinary precision and accuracy since we are detecting temperature variations of the order of magnitude of $1°$, not tenths of a degree or hundredths of a degree. Therefore, a temperature-sensing device that will detect temperature differences of $1°$ is adequate. Also, it is not necessary that this temperature sensor have a zero time lag. In fact, a time lag of the order of 1 min would be satisfactory.

When the output of the temperature sensor is compared with the reference temperature, a signal will be given either to turn the valve on or to turn it off, as the case may be, and once again the time constant need not be a very small value. It will certainly be less than several minutes, but if it is several seconds it is quite adequate. Almost any component that we might use would probably consist of a relay and a solenoid valve, and the time constants here would be in the order of seconds, not minutes. Quite obviously, then, devices would be available that could perform these functions with no great difficulty.

The block diagram for this house heating system, shown in Fig. 9.8a, can be simplified to that shown in Fig. 9.8b for consideration of sensitivity. The sensitivities with respect to G_2 and H are the important ones, as was discovered in the discussion of the tank problem in Sec. 9-2.

The selection of a 2° drop in temperature as the increment to start the heating unit and of a furnace with a capacity of 60,000 Btu/hr fixes G_1 at a value of 60,000, divided by 2°, or 30,000 Btu/(hr)(°F), which is employed to raise the temperature of the air within the house and the house itself. The material to be heated is represented by the quantity $\rho c V$, where ρ is the density, c the specific heat, and V the volume. Since the output is θ and the input is 30,000 Btu/(hr)(°F), we write the conservation equation:

$$30,000 \, dT = \rho c V \, d\theta \qquad (9.22)$$

where dT is an increment of time.

Solving now for the ratio of output to input, we have

$$G_2 = \frac{\text{output}}{\text{input}} = \frac{\theta}{30,000} = \frac{1}{\rho c V (d/dT)} = \frac{1}{\rho c V D_t} \qquad (9.23)$$

where $d/dT \equiv D_t$ and $G_2 = K_2 G_2(D_t)$, with $K_2 = 1/\rho c V$.

It now becomes necessary to decide upon the value of $\rho c V$. If the outdoor temperature stays relatively constant and if the indoor temperature does not vary more than $\pm 2°$ from the control temperature, the temperature of the mass of the house itself will change very little. However, the temperature of the air within the house will change $\pm 2°$. Consequently, we could consider simply the air in the house as the volume V in the transfer function for G_2. On the other hand, if the house has been unheated for a long period of time and the floors, walls, and ceilings are all cold, then $\rho c V$ must include the mass of the house. We consider first, then, simply the mass of the air within the house in the calculation of $\rho c V$. This gives a value of 12,800 cu ft of air, as calculated in the earlier discussion. If we take the density of air for the present purpose as 0.07 lb/cu ft and the specific heat 0.24 Btu/(lb)(°F), the product $\rho c V$ is 218 Btu/°F. Hence the numerical value of K_2 is 0.0046°F/Btu.

Summarizing the values of the pertinent parameters, we have

$$H = K_3 = 1.0$$
$$G_1 = K_1 = 30,000 \text{ Btu/(hr)(°F)}$$
$$K_2 = 0.0046°F/Btu$$

The sensitivities of the system gain K_s, from Eqs. (7.30) and (7.31), are as follows:

$$S_{K_3}^{K_s} \cong \frac{-K_1 K_2 K_3}{1 + K_1 K_2 K_3} = -0.993$$

$$S_{K_2}^{K_s} \cong \frac{1}{1 + K_1 K_2 K_3} = 0.0072$$

The sensitivity with respect to K_3 is nearly unity under these circumstances, indicating that if the temperature measurement by the sensor is in error the final house temperature will be in error by essentially the same amount.

The low sensitivity with respect to K_2 is a clear indication of the power of the heating unit in relation to the mass to be heated. Even if the furnace were to deteriorate badly, the house could be heated effectively, although an interpretation of the figure 30,000 Btu/(hr)(°F) is necessary to clarify the significance of the sensitivity with respect to K_2.

The input to G_2 has been taken as 30,000 Btu/(hr)(°F). The net effective heating ability is actually 30,000 Btu/(hr)(°F) less the heat loss of the house, which is dependent on the outside temperature. If the heat loss is at the rate of 46,700 Btu/hr, as calculated earlier for the design point of 50°F temperature difference between inside and out, the net effective heating capacity is 13,300 Btu/hr. If we use this figure rather than 60,000 as before, the value of K_1 is 6660 Btu/(hr)(°F).

The sensitivities are then

$$S_{K_3}^{K_s} = 0.97$$
$$S_{K_2}^{K_s} = 0.0317$$

The sensitivity with respect to K_3 is changed very little by this more realistic analysis, and the sensitivity with respect to K_2 is very acceptable. The design can be considered satisfactory from this standpoint.

The compatibility considerations in this design are at the interface of the outputs of the temperature sensor H and the reference θ_r, at the interface of the output of the adder and input to G_2, and at the interface of the output of G_2 and the input to H.

In a house heating system, the temperature is usually sensed by a mechanical device that takes advantage of the expansion and contraction of metal with changing temperature. The output is then a position of an arm or contactor. The reference θ_r is a position of a pin or contactor. When the relative positions cause a contact to be made or broken, the signal for starting or stopping the furnace is given. This signal is usually in the form of an electric current that actuates a solenoid valve. Compatibility of voltages is necessary to assure actuation of the valve. The output of H and θ_r must be compatible in the sense that they must be properly oriented, one to the other, to make or break contact when the temperature requires such action.

The interface between the output of the adder and G_2 is the solenoid valve; if the voltage is correct, the valve will be properly actuated.

The interface between the output of G_2 and input to H is the contact surface between the temperature sensor H and the air in the house. It suffices here that the sensor be sensitive to air temperature; this requirement is easily satisfied by a strip of metal suitably shaped to give a motion related to temperature change.

The optimization of this system would probably be with respect to a criterion of comfort. Cost is seldom a major concern, since the house owner accepts the need for a heating system. If the cost is compatible with the total cost of the house, little more need be said. In colder climates the cost of operation is a consideration. The most effective control of this is insulation of the house, which reduces the heat loss. The control system itself can do little in this respect.

Optimizing with respect to comfort requires adjustment of the controls to balance the temperature fluctuation and the frequency of furnace operation to obtain an acceptable compromise. If the band of allowable temperature fluctuation is narrow, the frequency of operation will be high; if the band is wide, the frequency will be low. Both high frequency and large bandwidth are objectionable to the occupant of the house. An acceptable compromise is a function of the householder's personal wishes.

As a preliminary design of this system, the foregoing discussion will suffice. It has confirmed the adequacy of the concept of the on-off control rather than a continuously varying one. Further, it establishes that there was no need for error-rate correction. A detailed design would involve selection of components to fit the circumstances and test of the system in cold weather. Use of a more elaborate mathematical model in this simple situation would not be justified, whereas it might be needed for a hotel, office building, or industrial plant.

9.4. A Problem in Manufacturing and Inventory

The following example encompasses the design of a portion of a system in a manufacturing plant. This is not a feedback control system and does not have all the elements of the systems discussed previously. It is used to illustrate the application of certain techniques in the optimization of the design of a part of a system only.

Figure 9.11 shows schematically an industrial establishment which manufactures a single product, processing it from raw material to a packaged product in two forms, one for domestic sale and one for foreign sale. The plant exists, except for raw-material storage which is to be built. The remainder of the plant cannot be expanded during the first 2 years of operation because of lack of capital. The design problem is to decide upon the optimum size of raw-material storage and the number of units of manufactured product to be packaged for domestic sale and the number for foreign sale, to yield the maximum profit during the 2-year period. The data available to the designer are the following:

The cost in dollars of raw material per unit of manufactured product is given by the expression

$$C = 10 + 2e^{-N_p/5,000}$$

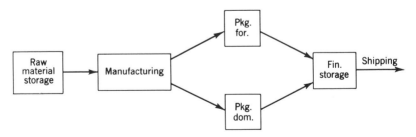

Fig. 9.11 Block diagram of manufacturing process.

where N_p is the number of units of material purchased in one lot for delivery at one time.

The cost of raw-material storage is estimated to be $5 per unit of domestic storage each year.

The maximum number of units that can be manufactured is 1,000 per day.

The packaging capacity is one of the following:

    For foreign sale: 650 units per day

    For domestic sale: 1,500 units per day

Foreign packages require twice as much storage space as domestic packages.

The total package storage available is either 40,000 domestic units or 20,000 foreign units.

The profit that can be made is 30 per cent greater on foreign sales than on domestic per unit.

The demand probability distribution for domestic and foreign packages is given in Table 9.1.

Table 9.1

No. of units per day	Number of days per year	
	Domestic	*Foreign*
0–100	1	5
101–200	2	10
201–300	5	15
301–400	12	20
401–500	20	30
501–600	30	70
601–700	80	50
701–800	40	30
801–900	30	20
901–1,000	20	10
1,001–1,100	10	0
1,101–1,200	5	0
1,201–1,300	3	0
1,301–1,400	2	0

The total number of days of operation per year is 260.

The solution of this problem is divided into three parts. The first is the determination of the optimum storage space for raw materials; the second is finding the storage requirements for foreign and domestic packages; the third is optimizing the distribution between foreign and domestic sales.

The optimization of raw-material storage depends upon the fact that the cost per unit for raw material is less if large quantities are purchased at one time, but storage costs are increased by large-quantity purchases. The cost C_s, incurred from purchase to delivery to the manufacturing process per unit, is

$$C_s = 10 + 2e^{-(N_p/5,000)} + \frac{5(N_p + 2,000)}{N} \tag{9.24}$$

where N_p is the number of units of raw material purchased at one time and N is the number of units produced per year.

This equation assumes the need for storage equal to the full shipment of raw material plus 2-days supply at 1,000 per day. This gives a small margin of safety for delays in delivery of raw material.

The cost per unit, when purchased in lots of 5,000 to 30,000, broken down into purchase price, cost of storage, and total cost, is given in Table 9.2.

If a single unit were purchased, the price would be approximately $12; as the number increases, the price approaches $10. The cost of storage starts at a minimum of zero when raw material is not stored but is purchased as needed and increases to a maximum of

Table 9.2

Number purchased at one time	Purchase price	Cost of storage	Total cost
5,000	10.736	0.134	10.870
10,000	10.270	0.231	10.501
15,000	10.100	0.327	10.427
20,000	10.036	0.423	10.459
25,000	10.013	0.520	10.533
30,000	10.005	0.615	10.620

\$5.05 if an entire year's supply is purchased in a single lot. The variation in cost is therefore from \$12, when items are not stored, to \$15.05 when a year's supply is purchased, with a minimum of about \$10.427 when lots of 15,000 are purchased.

The existence of an optimum value of N_p is apparent, since the first term of Eq. (9.24) decreases with increasing N_p and the second term increases directly with N_p. Minimizing C_s can be accomplished by differentiating with respect to N_p; thus,

$$\frac{dC_s}{dN_p} = \frac{-2e^{-(N_p/5,000)}}{5,000} + \frac{5}{N} = 0$$

Transposing, $\quad e^{-(N_p/5,000)} = \dfrac{12,500}{N}$

Inverting, $\quad e^{N_p/5,000} = \dfrac{N}{12,500}$

Taking logarithms, $\quad \dfrac{N_p}{5,000} = \ln \dfrac{N}{12,500}$

The annual production is $N = 260,000$ units; therefore,

$$N_p = 15,150$$

This confirms the figure of 15,000 units shown in Table 9.2. The construction of storage space to accommodate a 17-day supply is therefore economical.

We next investigate the storage requirements for foreign and domestic packages of finished product. Reference to the demand distribution table (Table 9.1) reveals a characteristic for each of the two items as given in Table 9.3.

These data are summarized in Fig. 9.12 in the form of a plotting of total demand and total supply as a function of total time, arranged from smallest to largest demand. This plotting can be used to find the maximum amount of storage that could be needed for either foreign or domestic packages.

The summation of demand against time in this form is the equivalent of the assumption that demand will occur in the order of smallest demands first, increasing to greatest demand. This is not implied in the demand distribution function, which gives simply the number of days of each demand for either the domestic or the foreign

Table 9.3

Aver. no. of units per day	Number of days		Number of units		Summation of demand		Summation of days	
	Dom.	For.	Dom.	For.	Dom.	For.	Dom.	For.
50	1	5	50	250	50	250	1	5
150	2	10	300	1,500	350	1,750	3	15
250	5	15	1,250	3,750	1,600	5,500	8	30
350	12	20	4,200	7,000	5,800	12,500	20	50
450	20	30	9,000	13,500	14,800	26,000	40	80
550	30	70	16,500	38,500	31,300	64,500	70	150
650	80	50	51,000	32,500	82,300	97,000	150	200
750	40	30	30,000	22,500	112,300	119,500	190	230
850	30	20	25,500	17,000	137,800	136,500	220	250
950	20	10	19,000	9,500	156,800	146,000	240	260
1,050	10	0	10,500	0	167,300	. . .	250	
1,150	5	0	5,750	0	173,050	. . .	255	
1,250	3	0	3,750	0	176,800	. . .	258	
1,350	2	0	2,700	0	179,500	. . .	260	

package and indicates nothing whatsoever about the order in which these demands might occur. However, by making the assumption that all the days of small demand occur first and that the demand increases continuously with time, we calculate the maximum amount of storage that could be required for any given rate of manufacture. If the rate of production is 500 units per day, we represent total supply to date by a straight line starting at the origin and increasing at the rate of 500 units per day. Thus, at the end of 100 days, production totals 50,000 units.

At the end of the same period of time, after all the smaller demands are summed, comparison of total production with total demand up to that time can be made. If the production exceeds the demand, storage is required to take care of this surplus. For example, comparing supply and domestic demand with a production rate of 500 units per day, we find that at the end of 40 days 5,200 more units have been produced than could be sold. Consequently, space to store this number must be available to maintain production rate. From this point on, the rate at which demand occurs is greater than the rate of production, and at the end of about 100 days total

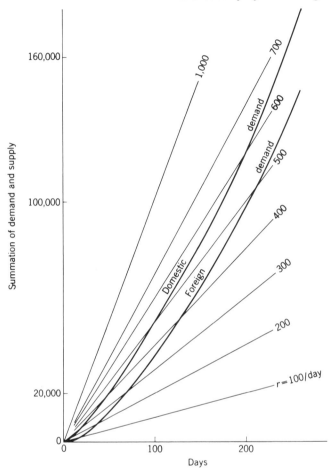

Fig. 9.12 Mass diagram of supply and demand and various supply rates.

supply and demand are equal, and there is no further need for storage. It is apparent, therefore, that this analytical tool will help to solve the storage problem in a very elementary manner.

The storage capacity has a maximum of 40,000 domestic units or 20,000 foreign, and we are able to package either 650 units for the foreign market per day or 1,500 for the domestic trade. In addition, maximum production is limited by the manufacturing process, not by the packaging, and a maximum of 1,000 units per day can be manufactured.

In maximizing the profit, we shall make use of each of the facts noted above, plus the knowledge that the profit on foreign sales is 30 per cent more than on domestic. We proceed now with the analysis of this aspect of the problem, using the techniques of linear programming developed in Chap. 6.

We let the number of units packaged for foreign sale equal N_F and the number for domestic sale equal N_D. We know that 650 units of foreign items can be packaged per day, or 1,500 for domestic; hence we can write, for the time T to package one item of each type,

Domestic:

$$T_D = \frac{1}{1,500} \text{ day}$$

Foreign:

$$T_F = \frac{1}{650} \text{ day}$$

and it follows that

$$\frac{N_F}{650} + \frac{N_D}{1,500} = 1$$

or $2.31 N_F + N_D = 1,500$ (9.25)

Now, since capacity for manufacturing is limited, we write

$$N_F + N_D = 1,000$$ (9.26)

The packaged storage is limited, and we let

N_{FS} = number of foreign packages in storage
N_{DS} = number of domestic packages in storage

Then the maximum storage capacity is

$$2N_{FS} + N_{DS} = 40,000$$ (9.27)

We must now relate the number of packages in storage to the packaging rate. From Fig. 9.12 we obtain the following facts, noting that the storage required is the maximum vertical distance between an accumulated supply line and the accumulated demand line.

Production rate	Storage required	
Domestic or foreign	*Domestic*	*Foreign*
	(No. of packages)	
100	50	250
200	250	1,250
300	800	3,000
400	2,000	7,500
500	5,000	15,000
600	10,000	25,000
700	22,000	40,000
800		

These are shown graphically in Fig. 9.13.

Approximate equations for the relationship between storage requirement and production rate are sufficiently accurate for our purposes. They are very good at high rates of production, and this is most important. These equations are

$$\text{Domestic storage} = N_{DS} = 2.49 \times 10^{-8} N_D{}^{4.2} \quad \text{packages}$$
$$\text{Foreign storage} = N_{FS} = 1.1 \times 10^{-4} N_F{}^{3.0} \quad \text{packages}$$

These relationships can be used to replace N_{DS} and N_{FS} in Eq. (9.27); thus,

$$2.2 \times 10^{-4} N_F{}^{3.0} + 2.49 \times 10^{-8} N_D{}^{4.2} = 40,000 \qquad (9.28)$$

Although this is not a linear equation, it can be used with Eqs. (9.25) and (9.26) in deciding the best rates of producing for foreign and domestic sales to optimize the profit.

Equations for manufacturing capacity and packaging capacity are shown graphically as straight lines in Fig. 9.14. This is possible since there is a linear relationship between the number of units for foreign production and the number of units for domestic production, both with respect to manufacturing and packaging. In Fig. 9.14, a line derived from the relationships shown graphically in Fig. 9.13 is shown. If we are packaging 700 units for domestic sale, we require a storage space of 22,000 units. This leaves 18,000 units for storage for foreign sales. However, foreign items require twice as much

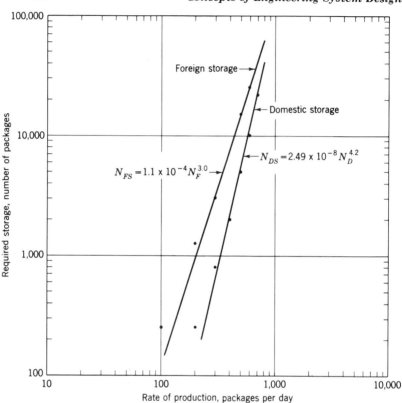

Fig. 9.13 Graphical determination of equations for storage requirements.

storage space; hence we can store only 9,000 items for foreign sale when we are manufacturing 700 units for domestic sale. This limits foreign production, as we see in Fig. 9.14, to 430 units per day. This is shown in Fig. 9.14 as point 4. Each other point on the packaged-storage line has been obtained in this manner. The points marked 1, 2, and 3, respectively, in Fig. 9.14 represent those which should be considered when investigating the profit situation.

The profit P is given by the expression

$$P = N_D + 1.3 N_F$$

Lines of constant profit have intercepts on the horizontal axis given by

$$N_D = P$$

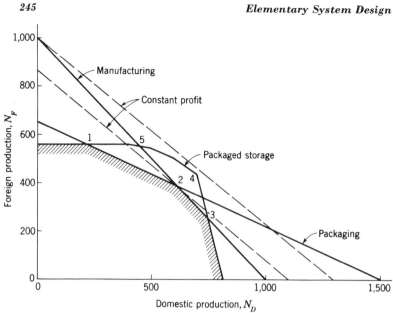

Fig. 9.14   Analysis of profit and storage relationships.

and on the vertical axis by

$$N_F = \frac{P}{1.3}$$

We show a line of constant profit that goes through the two points $N_D = 1,300$ and $N_F = 1,000$, and one that goes through point 2. The total profit is greater for constant-profit lines, the further the line is from the origin.   Point 2 represents a possible operation and is farthest from the origin in terms of a constant-profit line.

The profits corresponding to points 1, 2, and 3 are tabulated below:

Point	N_D	N_F	P
1	215	560	943
2	620	380	1,112
3	750	250	1,075

Clearly, point 2 yields the maximum profit among the three points considered.   That these are the points to be considered is clear when we observe that operation is possible only within the area bounded by the coordinate axis and the lines shaded on the side toward the origin.   The area upward and to the right of this shaded line is not a possible area of operation, since either manufacturing, packaging, or storage imposes a limit.   The method of operation for the factory that will yield a maximum profit under the restrictions set by the limitation of space and equipment at the time of the design is therefore represented by point 2.

Figure 9.14 can be used for further study if we wish to investigate the best method of improving the profit situation for the company.   An ideal situation should be represented by the three lines for manufacturing, packaging, and storage, parallel to the maximum-profit line, coincident one with the other and as far as possible from the origin.   We note that the packaging capacity with respect to foreign sales is a limiting factor, since the line representing this function is low at the left end.   The manufacturing line is not really bad, and since there is no difference in manufacturing between domestic and foreign sale items, there is not much that we can do about this except increase capacity.

The packaged storage places very severe limitations on the expansion of the activity.   For example, if we were to expand the capacity for packaging units for foreign sale by increasing it to 850, we would remove the restriction placed by packaging on the operation, and manufacturing would be the limiting factor.   The new point of maximum profit would be point 5, the intersection of manufacturing and storage lines.   This would yield a profit of 1,161 units, an increase of almost 5 per cent in the profit of the operation.   An increase in manufacturing capacity to 1,150 units per day would remove the restriction placed by manufacturing under the present circumstances.   Figure 9.15 shows the result of the operation.   The maximum profit is given by the operation described by point 6 in Fig. 9.15, with $N_D = 700$ and $N_F = 430$.   The profit is 1,259 units.   At point 7, with $N_D = 600$ and $N_F = 500$, there is not a great deal of difference, since the profit is 1,250.   Total production under these circumstances is 1,100 units per day in one case, and 1,130 in the other, under the maximum permitted by the new manufacturing setup with a capacity of 1,150.   In addition, the packaging operation is close to capacity, as indicated by the proximity of both points 6 and 7 to the packaging-operation line.

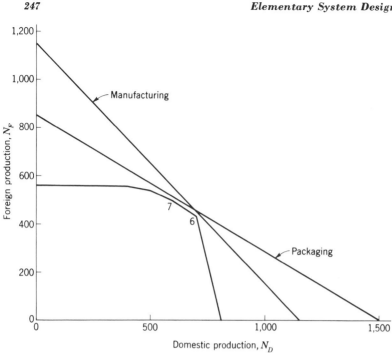

Fig. 9.15 Analysis of effect of packaging capacity on profits.

With this material at hand, it is possible to make an economic
study to establish the best procedure for increasing the capacity and
profit of the operation. The cost of increasing the manufacturing
capacity and the cost of increasing the packaging capacity are added,
and the annual cost of this change is compared with the increase in
profit. If there were a net increase in profit, the change would be
justified.

The method used to calculate the required maximum amount of
storage of finished, packaged goods has been overly conservative. A
better estimate of storage requirements in the case of plant expansion
can be obtained. The estimates were based on the concept that the
maximum is fixed if the demand is arranged in order of increasing
value. The demand is statistically distributed; hence it is extremely
unlikely that all the small demands would occur first and all the
large demands at the end of the year, unless something influences the
time distribution in this way. Holiday buying has such an influence.

We assume, then, that we know nothing more than the fact that

Table 9.4

$$r = 380$$

R	N	$\dfrac{r}{R}$	$\dfrac{r^2}{R^2}$	$\dfrac{N}{\Sigma N}$	$\left(\dfrac{r}{R}\right)^2 \dfrac{N}{\Sigma N}$
50	5	7.600	57.7	0.0192	1.110
150	10	2.530	6.40	0.0385	0.247
250	15	1.520	2.31	0.0577	0.133
350	20	1.090	1.19	0.0769	0.092
450	30	0.845	0.714	0.1154	0.082
550	70	0.692	0.480	0.2691	0.129
650	50	0.585	0.342	0.1924	0.066
750	30	0.507	0.257	0.1154	0.030
850	20	0.448	0.201	0.0769	0.015
950	10	0.400	0.160	0.0385	0.006
	260			1.000	$E(r^2) = $ 1.910

demand is statistically distributed, as indicated in the tabulation. We consider operation in accordance with the description of point 2 in Fig. 9.14, wherein we show a production of 380 units for foreign distribution and 620 for domestic. We define the ratio of the rate of production, 380 units per day, to the mean rate of consumption, 562 units per day, as the quantity $\rho = 380/562$. We calculate the expected value of the magnitude of the storage required for foreign production as follows: Although it is beyond the scope of the present discussion, it can be shown that $E(s)$, the expected value of the storage in this case, is given by

$$E(s) = \rho + \frac{E(r^2) - \rho}{2(1 - \rho)} \tag{9.29}$$

It remains to calculate the value of $E(r^2)$, which in this case is $E(r^2/R^2)$, since r itself is a constant and R varies; this is shown in Table 9.4.

Upon substitution of the numerical value of $E(r^2)$ in the expression for the expected value of the storage, we find that

$$E(s) = 2.57$$

The expected value of the storage requirement for foreign goods is equal to 2.57 times the average daily production, or the storage requirement for the foreign shipment F_s is

$$F_s = 2.57 \times 562 = 1{,}440 \text{ packages}$$

This requires a total of 2,880 units of storage, since foreign storage requirements are twice that of domestic. This value of 2,880 units compares with the maximum requirement for foreign storage at a daily production rate of 380 units, equal to 12,200, shown in Fig. 9.13. One would be prudent to provide storage for more than the expected value since this is a weighted average, but provision for twice this amount would certainly be adequate.

Similar calculations can be carried out for various rates of foreign production; results of this calculation are shown in Fig. 9.16. It is apparent here that, as the daily rate of production, r, approaches the average rate of potential sales, 562, the required storage increases greatly. In fact, it can be shown that, if the production rate is

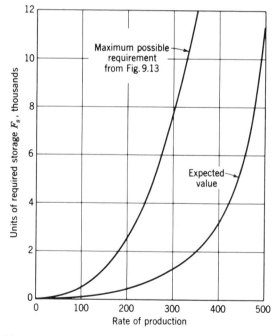

Fig. 9.16 Estimated storage requirements for foreign packages.

exactly equal to the potential sales average, the required storage approaches infinity. If a plant expansion were contemplated and storage requirements were to be determined for increased packaging and manufacturing rates, the procedures outlined thus far could be applied, and calculations using expected values of the storage requirements would be much more appropriate, especially if storage requirements were to prove restrictive in the expanded production schedule.

This is a partial solution to the problem of designing a system in the manufacturing process described above. We shall not, therefore, discuss in detail the various features of the design that have been considered in each other system. This exercise has been for the purpose of illustrating the application of certain techniques, such as linear programming, in optimizing elements of a system.

If one were to consider the complete design of this manufacturing system, including inventory control, quality control, and optimization of the manufacturing process itself, there would be involved all the detailed procedures described in the previous examples. For example, inventory control would encompass problems in feedback control. The principles are the same as in the other examples, but time constants and other parameters would be of different orders of magnitude.

References

Asimow, Morris: "Introduction to Design," Prentice-Hall, Inc., Englewood Cliffs, N.J., 1962.

Doebelin, E. O.: "Dynamic Analysis and Feedback Control," McGraw-Hill Book Company, New York, 1962.

Goode, H. H., and R. E. Machol: "System Engineering," McGraw-Hill Book Company, New York, 1957.

Gosling, W.: "The Design of Engineering Systems," John Wiley & Sons, Inc., New York, 1962.

Hall, Arthur D.: "A Methodology for Systems Engineering," D. Van Nostrand Company, Inc., Princeton, N.J., 1962.

Index